# The Rise and Fall of a Jamaican Don

## By

## Andre M. Porter

First published by 1stBooks 12/03/04

ISBN: 1-4033-3009-3 (e)
ISBN: 1-4033-3010-7 (sc)
ISBN: 1-4033-3011-5 (hc)

Library of Congress Control Number: 2002105736

Printed in Canada


This book is printed on acid-free paper.

# Acknowledgments

All praises due unto GOD. Thank you for life, health, strength and your everlasting love. Without you there would be no me. I would also like to thank me for having faith in myself knowing I alone could make my dreams a reality. To my parents, thank you for your guidance and tough love. My sisters and brothers. Tracy, Tricia, Sasha, Shauna, David and Michael AKA Chucky. Love for life. Jenny, you're the mother that never gave birth to me. Jamila thanks for keeping it real. HR. inc, in a secret society all we need is trust. Thanks to my family for keeping me in your prayers. S.I.L.K family, we can only get stronger. My cousin Joan. To the women who brought my kids into this world, thanks for giving me reasons to live. Myca-che, Tavina and Prince (Andre Porter JR). To all the people who thought I was never going to do anything positive with my life, your negative energy makes me stronger. Keep in mind my best is yet to come. Miss Guthrie thanks for being my angel when I needed one. Joyce thanks for re-fueling my hopes when my tank was on E. Susanne Bernsten and Frank of the Camden Free Public Library. Larry Miles of La Unique African Books in Camden NJ… NUFF RESPECT. Eugene Hopkins, Senior Account Manager, and Trina Lee, Account Manager of my book at AuthorHouse. Judith "Sunshine" Martin & Sophia Pearson from the Caribbean Network Society and Island Flava TV, thanks for your time and energy. All the radio personalities, Editors and cable TV host who said they were preparing me for Oprah…thanks in advance. Cash from Flawless Red for all the hype. Paramount respect to actor Paul Campbell : Dancehall Queen, The Lunatic,

Third World Cop, and Top Shottas to name a few. You are the "Bob Marley" of Jamaican cinema. Charmaine...thanks for being my sunshine. A special note to all Jamaicans, we have one of, if not the most unique culture. Until we unite, our talents and possibilities will continue to be limited. Our island needs our help to grow as a nation, not as a person. Out of many, we are one people.

"The only thing I love more than being alive is being a Jamaican
The last four letters of my nationality says I can
So my plan is to achieve the dreams I believe
While some act like Americans
The power of Reggae has the world talking like Jamaicans
Open your eyes and realize our strength"

Thanks for reading a voice from the ghetto of life. If I forgot to thank you or anyone else please excuse my memory. I truly appreciate the contributions you made to make the success of this book. ONE LOVE.

WITH YOUR SUPPORT AND THE POWER OF MY ISLANDS MUSIC THIS BOOK CAN BECOME A BOX OFFICE HIT. THANKS FOR YOUR VALUED SUPPORT AND TELL A FRIEND TO TELL A FRIEND.

*Jamaican Author.*

# Vision of A Movie

Thanks in advance for taking the time to read my work. I had no idea that I would have written and publish a book. My aim was to become a Lawyer, but God has a way of changing our direction and leading us to true destiny. I am grateful to HIM for doing so. A vision led to movies such as The Godfather, Scarface, King Of New York, New Jack City and Top Shottas to name a few. This book is not to promote the violence associated with my Island, but is my vision of a movie.

*When reading keep in mind this story was written by a man on the run for his life and did not have a chance to edit his manuscript before disappearing. The woman he last spoke to was asked to mail a package with this story. Instead she sent what your about to read to a publisher. This is only 1/3 of the story and introduction to his trials and tribulations. Again keep in mind it was not edited before being printed as this is the raw version of what he documented.*
*A.P*

# Reviews For Vision of A Movie

"A unique story from one of the most unique cultures in America, but this is not just a Jamaican book."

*Kevin Riordan – Courier Post*

"When I first began reading this book I went at it with a preconceived notion of what a book should read like. Well I have learned to place all my preconceived notions on layaway…………..long term layaway. A magnificent undertaking given the circumstances."

*Lance Cmaeron – West Indian Times*

"Andre Porter is one determined writer. Despite obstacles and hurdles he refuses to make excuses. I see a bright future."

*Lolita Long – Jamaica Gleaner*

"A true-life situation described in a captivating story. The meat shop gave me goose bumps. I honestly can't find words to describe this book but would pay to see the movie."

*Joycelyn Gardner – X-News*

"A Jamaican Mafia! Good luck Andre keep writing"

"If you think you've had your share of Mafia books, Andre Porter just introduced a new and dangerous breed"

"A fast paced unrelenting read that does not let go even beyond the last page. A very powerful story. Of all the movies I've done these characters are scared into my mind. This book is definitely a movie."

ON LINE BOOK SELLERS SUCH AS AMAZON.COM & BARNES & NOBLES HAS CUSTOMER REVIEWS AND 4 STAR RATINGS. HERE IS WHAT TWO READERS HAD TO SAY.

"I think he did a good job as a first time writer. The style he used made the story real in a way that I could see the man running…the bodies in the meat shop…..Blade in the coffin….the restaurant……it was just a good story. I will definitely be going to see this as a movie."

"I have never been a person to read this type of novel but the title alone made me want to read it. I think the author will become an established one if he continues to do as he has done. I gave it 5 stars because as a Christian he made me feel apart of the Mafia he wrote about. Also his unique way of telling the story. I hope he was not involved. Good story telling Mr. Porter."

*Unknown Reader*

I WOULD LOVE TO KNOW WHAT YOU THINK. PLEASE SEND ME AN E-MAIL AT

ANDREP1977@YAHOO.COM

## New Book Coming Soon

# MIRROR AND THE REFLECTION

**BASED ON THE LIFE OF A CHILD CAPTIVATED BY A RELIGION NOW A BISHOP IN SEARCH OF IMMORTALITY AS A SPIRITUAL LEADER...... MORE POPULARLY KNOWN AS AN OBEAH MAN.**

"I alone have seen the mysteries my eyes have seen. I alone have walked my path. Do the things I have done and I alone will stand before God to answer for my sins. My life has been a blessing and a curse, not by choice, but I was born with a gift and had to play the hand life delt me. They brought more than slaves from Africa, Revival is a part of our rich culture. Some may say the supernatural does not exist, let me take you on a journey into my life."

*Bishop Robert Croll*

First 5000 copies of the book features a double CD with a live interview with the BISHOP.

Give ear unto my prayers oh Lord and hear my cry
Your always faithful while others fake and lie
Thanks to your kindness we have the gift of life
Thanks for giving us the gift of life.

This is dedicated to my Grand parents... I hope your souls have found a place in heaven

# Table of Contents

## Forgive Me For My Sins Oh Lord or Take My Soul And Give It To An Unborn Saint.

I was walking along Flatbush Ave thinking about life while fearing death. I have been on the run for the past three months, death has been looking for me, and I have no place to hide. Here I am standing at what seems to be a dead end road and my life has nowhere to turn. The sprits I thought were locked away in hell, the deepest depths of hell have come back to life. My darkest secrets and deadliest deeds from my past have come back to put an end to my future. I have seen things I should not have seen and have been forced to do things the bible say we should not do. Now I must pay the wages of sin.

A Black MPV has been following me for the past two weeks since I got back to Brooklyn. I didn't pay it much attention that's until it pulled alongside me and I saw them. Without thinking twice, I started running. I know I wont be able to run forever, but I will as long as I can. I had already gained considerable distance and began to seek help. They have murdered all those who have tried to assist me in the past. Thanks be to God I was always three steps ahead. I thought Brooklyn would be the perfect place to hide since the Gambinos and FBI had them on their most wanted list.

The first door I knocked on no one answered. The second was a Puerto Rican woman that could not understand a word I was saying. The third door a man looked out his window then closed his blinds and turned off his lights. I could feel their presence getting closer as the sand in my hourglass was down to a few grains. I thought I was sweating from all that running but when I looked at my Grey shirt it was red. My body was stained with my own blood. I have never been shot before and this was no time to panic.

I crawled into the closest Dumpster and peeked through the lid as I tried to identify the fourth person with them. I stayed there until the night went back to its former silence then went in search of medical assistance. A few blocks down I saw a house with a cross on the door hoping that it represented a Christian who would be willing to help. A woman in her mid-forties opened the door but as soon as she saw the blood and the smell from the garbage she attempted to close it. Even though I begged her to help me she still refused.

"Miss please, I need your help, if you do not help me they will kill me. Just hide me for an hour and I will be gone as soon as it is safe enough. Please help me, I don't want to die."

My body was beginning to feel numb and my vision was less clear. Now I was getting scared. I did the only thing I could do. For the past six months I have been living in fear not knowing when things I kept in the dark would come to light. Three months ago they discovered the truth and since then I have been on the run. I began making a journal describing events that have occurred since meeting them a few years ago. I gave her the journal I had been guarding with my life along with the instructions I had already outlined and all my valuables. As soon as I saw them turn the corner, I tried to run.

Dear Reader,

Due to the nature of this text and possible danger involved, I will not disclose my name or any personal information that might link me to this publication or anything associated with it. A month ago, I had a very unforgettable experience as I think I might have witnessed one of New York's biggest unsolved murders. I had just came home from work and no longer than an hour later there was a wounded man at my door begging me to help him. I did not know who he was or where he was from so naturally I was reluctant towards letting him in my house. Especially a wounded man. He seemed terrified by what or who was chasing him. He handed me what seemed to be a manuscript and all his valuables and begged me to follow the instructions, as that was his last wish.

I should have reported it to the police and I know I may go to jail for not doing so, but there was something about him that captivated my spirit and led me towards doing this.

A few minutes later after he disappeared into the dark gunshots disturbed the once silent night and the same MPV he described left tire marks at the end of our block. In the morning, there were no reports of a missing person or dead body. Nothing about the shots fired was mentioned in the news or in the local paper. I wonder what happened. Yesterday on my way to work, I realized that I left my Metro card and had to return home. While searching for it I stumbled on the manuscript and remembered the promise I had made that wounded stranger a few weeks ago. Since the post office was across the street from my work place, I thought I would mail it at my earliest convenience.

The train ride to work is almost two hours long and is usually boring and exhausting. I decided to see what was so important to him. If I had known who he was or the people he was involved with, I would have never opened my door. The story was so compelling that I missed my stop and ended up being suspended and almost fired for my consistent lateness. The story was nothing compared to the info I found from researching old newspapers at the public library. He was associated with the ROCK, a Jamaican gang that became involved with the Mafia. Numerous unsolved murders, drug trafficking, loan sharking, tax violation, illegal firearms and the list went on and on. I guess the journal he made was his experience of living by their code of honor. A code he might have died to protect. He knows where bodies have been disposed and may have failed to protect his own.

This is what was recorded in his journal, UNEDITED, and possibly true. Now I would like to share with you what he gave to me that night. It seems to be only half the story, hopefully the person it's being sent to will take it upon him or herself to share the remainder with you. May God bless that stranger's soul.

Yours truly,
UNKNOWN.

# Introduction

Before I start telling you this story, let me first tell you a little about myself and how this all began. I represent a small portion of the people who come from all over the world in search of a better life in the land of opportunity. America is the only place on this earth where you can go to bed broke and wake up being a millionaire. The country where dreams are born and fantasies are fulfilled. I am from the Caribbean. Some of us are from Haiti, Trinidad, Bahamas, ST Lucia, Puerto Rico ect. Me, I represent Jamaica. An island rich with talent and culture, but its people dwell in poverty.

I was born in Kingston during the mid seventies when Bob Marley began his musical career, the first child to both parents and the first male born in ten years in the family. I was also the first in my family to get a government scholarship to Jamaica College, but later I had to be transferred to Cornwall College as my father and oldest sister migrated to the USA. I moved to Westmoreland to live with my mother while awaiting my Green card opportunity which came a few years later. I was among those in their teenage years dreaming of all the beautiful things the movies and BET showed us that America had to offer. Judging from those who came home with their designer clothes, rental cars, a house almost finished and seemingly the world in their pockets. The way their speech had changed and how the cold weather made them look fresh. Their stories of beautiful women, cars, easy to earn money and the movie stars they saw in person.

I used to close my eyes and dream of America. Thinking of all the things I would have and how much respect I would get when I returned with as many Benjamin as I could earn. Some of us are still beginning to realize that this country is not what people say it is. America is what you make of it. all those who have had the opportunity to come here wish those back home could realize how difficult it can be to survive here. It may be the land of opportunity, but can also be the coldest and toughest place you've ever known.

While waiting to hear from those who have left you behind in search of prosperity and wealth, you pray daily for their safety and that they will remember you. then the family letter comes and your name is not mentioned at all. you suddenly feel betrayed, they promised to drop you a line and never forget you no matter what. A few weeks later a barrel comes and you get a pants, shirt or a pair of Nike sneakers. Your faith has been renewed and you go to bed early so the day you will wear it comes closer. Then before you know it, your sitting at the airport waiting to experience your first flight. You sadly said good-bye to the ones you love, left your family in tears of joy because your on your way to a better life.

It was hard telling your friends that you've known all your life you wont be there to play ball tomorrow, but even harder not being able to tell your little brother good-bye because he was out of town. The next day you wake up in the environment you always dreamed of.

Your new family tries to ensure you that you should make yourself comfortable and at home but you keep silent and by yourself. A week later your talking a little and still trying to adjust to the food. Three months later you can go to the mall by yourself and know where to find the nearest Western Union. Six months later you wake up and realize that life in America is not as easy as you thought it was. You have bills to pay, yourself to maintain and an unpredictable weather to deal with. Some of us go back to school and work, while others do what they have to in order to survive.

This is a story of seven such kids who came from the same island with similar dreams. I was living in Camden New Jersey, a city ranked among the poorest in the nation being generated by drugs and crime. I was too educated not be living the American dream while thugs earned their Masters Degree in the street game that brought them fortune and fame.

I was a Tele-marketer earning $ 6.15 an hour and lost my job. That was just not my day and ended up being in the wrong place at the wrong time. I went to see what my weed doctor had in store for my financial migraine headache and the police came by to raid the spot. Jail was not on my agenda so I got away by stealing a car and ended up in the Big Apple, New York City. I sold the car and used the money to rent an apartment, drained out every credit card I had and set out to make my dreams a reality.

My second week in Brooklyn I went to a party hosted by some Jamaicans, it was entertaining compared to those I used to attend in Camden. Soon I became a loyal patron and met a Don named ICE, he was also a Jamaican. I had a very impressive portfolio and he agreed to invest in my ideas. I had no idea what I was getting involved with a Jamaican Mafia until it was too late. Now all I have is this story to share with you.

# Chapter One

Much more than a leader
He was like a father to those who knew
Like a rose from concrete
That's how he grew

Being a parentless child,
He turned to the streets
Drifted across the seas
And landed on America beats

Never being a kid
He matured into a thug
Didn't bother with college
Packed heat and sold drugs

Having women on their knees
More often for him than for HIM
Never having fears,
But always being feared

Doing whatever possible
Just to get the job done
Robbery, Sex and Torture
Always having fun

A media generated role model
Money, Drugs and Hoes
The more money and power you have,
The more sorrowful woes

Now the sting of death
Has crept and left
The man we knew as Blade,
Is laid to rest
But as we say in Jamaica
"No problem man"
The rise and fall,
Of a Jamaican Don.

That was the first time I went to a funeral, a very close friend had died a few years ago and I was unable to attend. I presume Blade must be at least halfway comfortable. He was somewhat a perfectionist, yet a simpleton. A little man with a big heart like Allen Iverson. It all happened so fast, life was being so good, none of us thought it would have ended like this. At least what was left of us. The Rock had lost the man who helped them mature into successful businessmen and had built the first Jamaican Mafia.

"He that over cometh shall inherit all things, and I will be his God he shall be my son."

Rev 21:7 Ashes to ashes dust to dust. Those were the final words before shot guns broke the bitter silence and filled the air with the honorable smell as we said farewell to a real Jamaican Don.

It began in the hallway of Liberty High School in Brooklyn NY, September 15, 1990. Romeo, a quarter- back with the IQ of a rat and leader of the White Panthers, a local racists school gang that built its rep by beating on all new students especially black ones. Today they chose the five boys they heard were from the most feared Caribbean Island, Jamaica. The Panthers had already surrounded their seemingly feeble adversaries and began issuing blows. Blade loved to see a good fight, but David was no normal kid. At the time he weighed no more than a hundred and twenty two pounds and each time he got knocked down he got up. Even though there were more than six of them beating on him, he just kept getting up and fighting back, you have to respect anyone with that type of courage.

A baseball bat being laid across the backs of everyone without a permanent suntan, which's how they met Blade interrupted the

2

commotion. Everyone dispersed to the sound of the whistle as the security guard approached the hallway. Unfortunately, they were caught and spent the remainder of the day in detention. There was a bit of uncertainty among them, should we say thanks or ask why did he bother to make our fight his and risk getting in trouble.

That was David, he later became Blade's right hand man. He was from Spanish Town and had only been in the United States for a few months. His dad was a mortician and really didn't have much time to raise a child. They say that police and pastors have the worst kids, I guess morticians do too and David was no exception. His dad decided to send him to the US after he got into one of his many fights at school and took his dads' gun. Luckily at that time he was not as good of a shooter as he now is. He got expelled and his dad was sentenced to a year in prison. As a result, David was sent to live with his uncle Chucky who was an alcoholic, a drunkard who had nothing inspirational to tell his nephew, except that there is no problem that a little Rum couldn't wash away.

I guess that's why D never really messed with alcohol or smoked, he rarely spoke, and when he did, whatever he said was taken seriously.

Rice was a coolie, Jamaican word for Indian. Blade gave him that name because that is all he ate, with meat of course, his real name was Kenton Palmer and was from a poor family and used to live in Kingston. He came to the United States on an educational trip and never returned. His school was having a trip to Disney World, one that most kids on the island dream of being apart of. Usually most families are not able to afford the trip and depend on relatives' abroad to pay for what seems to be a very costly vacation. To some it is a chance for their kids to experience the joy of flying. To others it is an opportunity to give their child a chance of having a better life by not returning. He renewed his relationship with his cousins who had been living in New York for the past twelve years.

He didn't really know them except for what he read in the letters and phone conversations. Blood is thicker than water, so family comes first no matter what. Rice always wanted to become a movie star he could tell the plot to any popular scene, but lacked the brain power to play lead role.

He mostly admired Wesley Snipes for the role that he played in New Jack City as Nino Brown. His only problem was that he didn't have the brains to control people minds. At least not like Blade could.

I'd say that Blade got here by destiny, almost like a fairy tale. He was from Portland, a parish known for it's rich vegetation of bananas and coconuts; two of our islands major export crops. His father had run off on his mother when she was 8 ½ months pregnant, he was to be the first child for both of them, then a few weeks later, gunmen robbed and raped his mother. One of the men used a knife to cut his mother across the belly and left her for dead, luckily she held on long enough to be rescued and gave birth shortly before dying.

After being sent from family member to family member to be raised, Blade was soon old enough to work. I guess learning independence at an early age is indeed vital to ones survival. On April 25, 1987, after loading a banana boat in Kingston where he know worked, he decided to take a nap before his next loading duty. He must have been really exhausted, because he woke up halfway across the Caribbean Sea heading towards the Statue of Liberty, the land of opportunity, the United States of America.

As I said, destiny must have been his case because he was able to use his quick thinking by unloading a few boxes from a container, throwing them over board, and occupy the available space. The rest as they say is history. After spending a few nights on the mean streets of Brooklyn he met Miss Guthrie she was a schoolteacher. When Miss Guthrie rescued him, she went to the City Hall and found a social security number that belongs to a dead person, someone that had been deceased for more than twenty years, that's how she managed to help allot of immigrants' get into school. She was a real angel that believed every child deserved a chance, a fair chance to get an education. In most cases, for families who come to the USA from any part of the world, getting into the school system can be a very difficult task, especially when and if that child is not 100% legal. Most times when the principal turns them down, she would look into the file and offer whatever assistance she could.

In appreciation for her willingness to help, the community once released fifty pure white doves on her birthday as a prayer for long life to her, I guess most prayers go unanswered. After he related his almost incredible story from birth, the two became one. When Blade drifted across the Caribbean Sea, his future was already written and awaiting him. For him pain would be love, but nothing could have prepared him for what was in store.

Then there was Garrett Anderson, a.k.a. G-Money; Rice gave that name to him. The two ran off on the same school trip, ended up in New York City and became best of friends. This was a different family case. Mr. and Mrs. Anderson had left their kids behind in Westmoreland to become farm workers; they never returned and had no intention of doing so. The school trip proved to be a vital opportunity to be with at least one of their siblings and he was chosen. G-Money became a music fanatic, to him music was like Wall Street and he was an investor very determined to make a mark in the music business. Garrett was the youngest in the crew, he had a natural charm that made women fall at his feet, they practically worshiped him. Some called him baby face; some call him the pride of the ghetto, most people liked him; those who didn't were just simply player haters. He had unlimited talents; dancing, singing, rapping, writing poetry, music, and a cold heart.

They said the first fight they got into as a crew he did the most damage. A crew from Queens came to take revenge for their friend who was beaten a few days earlier. That day no one was packing, and since Blade and David were not around, they thought it would be a walkover. When the fight started he ran to get his chopper, they thought he had deserted his crew, he came back and the least amount of stitches given was twenty-nine. Blade treated him like a little brother so he got away with things that no one else could.

Buju a.k.a. Andre Kerr, he had a green card and was from a solid family unit, mother, father and one brother, Armani. He was always high and drank Budweiser like water. He had started smoking weed at an early age; he and his brother were allowed to. Their mother was a Rasta woman and encouraged them to enjoy the herb of life and of wisdom. Nothing or no one bothered him, whenever something was on his mind you could easily know, he would light up a blunt and the problem just seemingly disappeared. Buju was always carefree but always cautious and was very protective of Armani. They were a fairly rich family, and so they were privileged to wear the finer collectibles, Armani took it upon himself to adopt his prospective alias from his favorite designer.

Last, but by no means least, Industry. They knew he was going to become a talk show host, a successful businessman or a gunsmith. He was always reading about guns and watched nothing but cartoons. I thought he was crazy when I first saw him. To be honest, to this very day we still do not know how he got here or where in Jamaica he lived. He was too young to remember how he got here and he'd become almost like a Yankee. He could talk anyone to sleep, somewhat a human radio with no batteries or electricity needed. All he did was talk morning noon and night. He too was from a fairly rich family and would use any opportunity given to talk about the things he had. Rice and David met him on the first day of school because he was talking about Jamaica, telling all lies to those who were willing to listen. His mother Miss Olive was a cook in a local Jamaican Restaurant in Brooklyn. She'd always be worried about her only child and being a single parent she had every right to be. Not only for security purposes, but the constant use of his mouth and the lies he told.

Industry got his name because of his constant urge to buy and sell things. That was how he made money, which's how they started making money.

They had now become friends and called themselves The Rock. They were much more than friends, they had become each other's guardians away from home. Blade was the oldest; he had more experience and was somewhat a young professional. He was their leader, well not really their leader. They started out as equals but over time decisions were made by his final word. The Rock was now popularly known as the Jamaican crew that no one in Liberty high wanted to fuck with period. They brought fear to school and sold it to the students at a reasonable price, soon they began to follow the traits of what most dons from Kingston had come to America and started on the streets. They were now selling weed in school.

Shabba was very notorious, one of the islands most wanted. He was from an area in Kingston called Water House home of those that killed the dead and made the living scared to live. He had killed a few policemen on the island and with the help of his employer, managed to beat he immigration system and ended up in Brooklyn NY. His son was killed outside the school gates on his twelfth birthday. His son was the first in the family to get a government scholarship to Kingston College and on December 23, 1984 he left for school thinking his parents had forgotten his birthday. That's what they wanted him to think, they were planning a surprise party and had invited a few of his close friends and his grandfather whom he had not seen in a long while due to the fact he was in the hospital.

There had been an ongoing high school gang war over who was going to win the Manning cup finals, the most prestigious soccer tournament for qualifying schools mostly in the Kingston area. St. Gorges College was the neighboring school and the other team in the finals. Shabba was pulling up as the student from K.C approached the Gorges student and stabbed him. As the wounded student fell, there was his son walking towards the car surprised to see him, suddenly gunshots made the music in the car seemed to lower, clapping at random. Then he realized that everything his son had learned in school that day was on the ground and the remainder of his brain leaking on the blood stained asphalt, he never got a chance to tell his first and only child happy birthday. Shabba got out the car and held his son as he trembled to death. The teenage shooter was still standing there as if he didn't realize the real dangers of a gun, or what it was capable of

When the police got there, he was still using his belt to squeeze the last breath from the teenager that shot his son. A police officer ran over to him and hit him across his back with the baton; he took the gun and did what he knew he had to do in order to get away. In Jamaica, not every time you get locked up you go to jail; you may be found dead, seriously. Now he was a major figure in Brooklyn and as they say, he had the streets on lock. One day after school Blade and his now posse decided to cook some curry chicken and rice, David was sent to the corner store. Shabba had a worker on the streets that always came up short with the count. He also attended their school only four days out of the school week, but was always seen in a phat ride and carried a pocket full of Benjamins to buy as many friends as he wanted.

He was a tenth grade student coming to school in rides that teachers in their fifth year of profession could not afford, all he drove was trucks on twenty-inch rims with television. After paying for the groceries, David was about to exit the store when he heard the four shots fired, across the street, Shabba had just shot and killed the kid. He then got into his Lexus and left, no one saw anything except David. A few days later he was detained by the police. The storeowner told the police that he may have seen what had happened as he was standing at the door to leave the store when the shots were fired.

They had also detained their suspect, as he was popularly known to use students as distributors and sellers of his drugs. They put David in a room and told him that they would give him anything he wanted if he pointed out the suspect they would do anything to get off the streets. David told them that he never saw anything. Ten hours later they were still asking him the same questions and he was still giving the same answers, I know nothing and I saw nothing, I guess that is why Blade trusted him so much. They became a secret society and all they needed is and was trust.

Two weeks later on their way home from school they were stopped by a female who gave David a package and told him it was a gift from Shabba. She told him that she knew he was smart enough to know what to do with it and that he would keep in touch then she left. The package had a pound of skunkweed and was worth near two thousand dollars. For a long time they had it hidden in their locker at school, no one wanted to take it to their home, the risk was too high, way too high. Buju kept smoking the weed blunt by blunt until one day he was caught by a student who instead of wanting to report him, wanted to buy some weed from him.

The next week Industry came to school with a pack of weed bags and they got started. In less than a month they had sold half of the weed. They never had that much money before and really did not know what to do with it. The summer was almost here, so they went shopping to get their gear up. At that time their parents and guardians were not going to spend that much money on name brand clothes while they had bills to pay, now they were wearing Air Jordan's worth half the rent. They told them they had after school jobs. Blade, he was just happy to be able to help Miss G with the bills, that way she could focus more on her health. Over the years she had gotten ill and it seemed she was getting worst instead of better. Then they started driving to school, soon grown women began to admire the high school posse that made being young seem like fun, so they rented whatever they wanted to make them feel like men. Blade was now in his final year of high school and his click was in the tenth grade. The prom was just around the corner and Blade had to attend. He left Liberty High in fine style and left his posse to rule.

The same kids he'd saved from being victims of a school fight had now become his army, a solid platoon who knew only one rule, whatever, whoever, whenever the Rock together. The Rock, loved by few, hated by many even our own.

# Chapter Two

School had become work. Their chill base was at Blades' house. Miss Guthrie had died a few months earlier and had left everything to him, the house her car and some money. He put some of her belongings in storage then transformed the four-bedroom house with a finished basement into his own castle that became their home away from home. The basement was huge, they did not have enough beds so they made a trade with an African named Johnny, a quarter pound of weed and one hundred dollars for three beds.

Every day they had a new set of girls, some of whom had become loyal freaks, just imagine schoolgirls in constant competition wanting to see who gave the best heads. Rice did most of the cooking. They didn't bother to waste money on fast food. Once in a while they would grab something from the Chinese store, Crown Fried Chicken or McDonalds. Most times their stove kept lit and a pot was boiling with something spicy.

Grades and attendance started to drop fast. Then for days no one went home or bothered to call so those worried about them would at least know they were ok, who cared? Money made them feel grown.

D had a very hot temper that was triggered by a very short fuse. He was not very fluent in Spanish and hated to be insulted, this was a lesson soon to be learned by his Spanish teacher Mr. Edwards.

"Mr. Crowl, could you please count to twenty in Spanish?"

D was not very fluent, and didn't want to be embarrassing himself.

"Mi nuh know how fi do it sir."

Mr. Edwards was unable to understand his reply.

"Mr. Crowl, could you be more civilized and speak English, we can't understand that Jamaican nonsense you just uttered."

His teachers comment made the students start laughing at D.

"Tu mama chocha Es muy grande Senor Edwards."

David had just done the unexpected; he had dissed what was labeled as being the toughest teacher.

By now the class was back to its former silence. The teacher walked down the isle to David's' chair and slapped him in his face and before anyone realized where this was going it happened, a student and teacher fight. They all had reached their final year in High school and were about to make today their last. Rice and Industry were in a different class and heard what was going on and soon joined in.

Using heavy-duty padlocks attached to chains, they assaulted three members of the faculty and sent two security guards to the emergency room. Their principal was not very fond of them and was eagerly awaiting the perfect reason to kick them out of school. They not only had the students scared, but a lot of teachers also feared them. They tried to tell the school board that Mr. Edwards had started the fight, but their long list of detentions and suspensions gave them no justice.

At the end of it they all got expelled. Their respective parents and guardians were also out of options of controlling them, with their track record at home, they also got kicked out. Blade was their only alternative so now six young men had to function as a family. The first six months went by comfortably, they each had jobs and maintained themselves, at least for the time being. Blade had two jobs, the fish store in the local market from 8am-12noon and as a security guard at the Century 21, a gigantic clothing outlet. This made shopping easy and cheap for the Rock. Each member came in on a specific day and basically walked out with whatever they wanted, the good stuff too.

Blade was always saving his money for real estate. His family lived in a rented house in Jamaica, something referred to as a Government yard by the late great Bob Marley in one of his many smash hits, No Woman No Cry. Blade thought he would make a great land lord. G-Money had somewhat developed his skills and started selecting on Thursday nights at The Q Club in Queens, that soon became their hangout spot. In order to avoid the natural hate that was born in the streets, they kept to themselves. Life was about to see just how strong they were. Blade became sick and soon lost both jobs, so did Buju for smoking a blunt while on break and Industry for wanting to act like the boss. Soon only Rice was bringing in an income and $7.15 an hour was not much to feed six men. The rest had already quit their perspective jobs and left no one with a source of income since selling weed had too much competition outside school.

The winter of 96 proved to be the worst. All their resources had almost been utilized. For the next two months, all they could afford to eat was Bagels, breakfast lunch and dinner, just Bagels. This was seemingly the coldest and meanest winter they had ever encountered. No money, not being able to have proper meals, unpaid bills and worst of all Buju had gotten his girl Sydonnie pregnant. Now the easy life started to seem not so easy, I guess that's when they began to realize that being responsible comes with responsibilities. Blade was always business minded, he had a few ideas, but never had a chance to make any of them a reality, the time was now, what did he have to loose? He knew that if the Chinese could come to America and do it, then so could he. They had their first meeting in the attic. This had always been Blade's off limit area to them, but tonight he was ready to let them into the dark world.

The attic had two significant items, an old oak table and a TV with a built in VCR. The table which was located in the far right corner, held a lit black candle, four glasses of water on each end, a bottle of Jamaican rum and the Bible opened at The Book of Psalms. The seventh Psalm was neatly highlighted. Beneath the Bible was a key. An old big key. Along with the TV were tapes of gangster movies, King of New York, Mobsters, New Jack City, Heat, The Professional, Godfather Part 1 and 2 and Scarface. Blade had met Priest in his earlier days. Priest was what's popularly known in Jamaica as an **Obeah Man.** He had taught Blade about laws of the underworld, a lesson that became a vital part of their lives. He was from Africa, possibly from the same tribe as Shaka Zulu, 6ft 4 inches tall, black as night and very serious.

Nothing could make him laugh, I heard he killed his father. They said his father was some sort of a royal figure and had many wives, his mother was one of many forced to marry their villages' noble warrior, a very abusive one. He returned home to see his mother tied to a tree half dead. She had refused to have sex with her husband, which is considered to be an act of defiance. Priest then known as Kongo, chopped his father until he was dead. He then took his fathers head and hung it on the entrance to his tent. The elders of the village told him he had to leave, he should have lost his life, but the justice he passed seemed fair compared to the treatment that was being given to his mother. Besides that, the other warriors feared him for killing one of the best among them; a few weeks later he ended up in Nigeria. There he met a team of explorers who hired him as their guide, they were on a search for rear specie of parrots found only in certain parts of the dense jungle.

After a few days of searching in vain, they got stranded and lost in the middle of no where and were attacked by a tribe of cannibals. With them having little or no experience of tribal war or basic survival skills, they stood there and watched as he single handedly killed four of the seven flesh eaters. In appreciation for his act of bravery, he was taken to the USA. The only thing he had to make a living from was his spiritual powers. He had little education, but judging from appearance, you could tell he was well maintained from whatever he did. Tape after tape, movie after movie. They all sat attentive. Just as each character in every movie played a vital part of their survival, so did each of them.

"Life is a movie and we're becoming some very desperate actors, we have to get the lead roles. Your life is a movie and we don't get a sequel, so live it to the fullest. None of these gangsters were given anything, including their respect. If we want respect we have to earn it or take it, if any of you want to go back and beg your family to take you back now is the time. If you decide to stay we will remain friends until we die."

Blade made it clear and quick, now it was time to hit the streets and eat.

Buju already had a gun, a 22, small but effective. He had to ride the train across town to see Sydonnie so he needed protection. Blade had two, a 9mm and a shotgun for special occasions, Blade handed his 9mm to David and quickly taught him the basics. Aim to the chest and shoot to kill, from what I have seen it was a lesson well learnt. Blade put the shotgun in a gulf bag he had and the hunt was on. They caught the number two train to Grand Station and went in their formation as planned. Blade, Rice and G-Money went forward and the rest followed. They knew a few Puerto Ricans who had a banging dope spot and tonight they were going to become a full course meal. What Blade did not know was that they too were in for a surprise.

The three approached the two Ricans and ordered four dimes, one of them went into the alley to get the goods while the other stood guard. By this time the remaining three were in their position and before the kid who was left to stand guard realized what was going on, Blade had the gun at his head. Then a shot was fired and Buju got hit in his left arm, Industry ran. The shoot out lasted for a little over five minutes. They had never killed anyone before and had no intention of doing so, but at the same time they had to do what ever it took to make sure they stayed alive. They had already made a plan B to meet at the train station if anything happened and that's where they caught up with Industry. They made sure that they left nothing, they took money and drugs.

No one spoke on the way home; the night's happenings had transformed six normal kids into the streets dark angles. Blade, he was already transformed. The story of what had happened to his mother had already made him cold, he never showed any emotions and they only saw him cry once, besides that, nothing. In one night the Rock had transformed themselves, they were no longer a crew, they had become something else. Almost like Tony Montana in his younger days.

The winter of 96 might have been their worst, but based on the facts of life, any situation has to get worse before it gets better. Money is a very valuable commodity, a commodity that was taken from all those who had it in abundance, despite race, color or creed. That Thanksgiving was observed, they were no longer struggling but bubbling, they had robbed almost every possible drug spot in operation in and around the area. Blade was now able to get his life long dream, they used most of their money to buy HUD houses. There were a lot of homes in the area being sold by the government at the sheriff sale, sometimes at a very low price, depending on the amount of tax owed. If the price were in their line of budget, they would buy the property.

Most times the taxes on the property were high so the price of the house was low. Their first step was to pay the taxes, do the necessary repairs, and then get them inspected to be rented later. At the time life seemed to be fun, but soon they began to realize that there was much more to life than just driving a hot car and having a few dollars to burn. Sure life can be a big party when your young, but who is going to have your back when it is all done. What happens when you wake up one morning and realize that the only thing that lasts forever is salvation? Blade wanted much more from life than just the simple things, he wanted all he could dream of and was determined to get it. Their first out of town operation took a member a prisoner of death, Armani.

The Silk Family was the number one crew in Philly, big ballers. They bought from the Italians; the Rock had no real beef with them, but in order to take over their block, they had to eliminate them. Right now the Silk Family had the market they wanted covered. They came to NY only to collect their weight and any money owed then went back to Philly. The Rock focused on the technique of development, one at a time beginning with the simplest ones, they sometimes combined techniques, but you must first learn to walk before you can run. For the moment they concentrated on what seemed to be relatively uncomplicated matters. Right now they had money, not big money. Robbery did not always generate much, especially when they had to buy guns and ammo, and pay lookouts so they would know when the cops were near. That money was used for ordinary expenses needed to stay alive in the grimey streets of NY. With the little they had left they bought another car.

David took five kilos of coke from Shabba on consignment. He figured that since Shabba really owed him more than just a pound of weed, granting him that favor would even things out. They paid some one to cook the coke and told the person to add a pinch of ammonia and baking soda to stretch it and give it the extra strength crack femes loved. Four in the morning on a cold winter day and six teenagers are on the streets giving out samples of the product that they called Express. Within a month they were easily making twenty thousand dollars every two weeks. They operated in shifts, three of them sold the crack from midnight to noon and the others had the other shift. All day every day, rain sun or snow. Soon the police were starting to become an obstacle so they had to get a few more lookouts. All they wanted was to gain enough so they could step up in the game.

The block they wanted to take over was owned by Silk. He used to live in Brooklyn before moving to Philly and becoming a Rastafarian; it was more a business than personal move. Now even though Silk was not living in BK, he still collected rent for the block, just as you pay rent for your apartment, you have to pay rent to sell on someone's block. You may be asked to pay a weekly fee, and keep in mind that it also depends on your street credit. I guess the amount they paid was beginning to hurt their pockets, or they just didn't want to pay. Armani had matured into a keen shooter and was eager to prove his skills, he convinced Blade that he could easily eliminate their obstacle. However he had one problem, he enjoyed using too many bullets on one victim.

The Silk Family had their headquarters on South Street, one of Philly's most popular and attractive business areas. They also operated a restaurant, an idea Blade soon capitalized.

The darkness was gathering and the ice-cold rain was fucking up everything. Traffic was a bitch; sidewalks were filled with Irish drunks celebrating St. Patrick's Day. Armani gripped the familiar handle of his glock 9mm, again he felt secure. He kept his hand on his gat in his pocket ready to open fire at first chance, a moment later he saw his target come out of the restaurant and leaped into the backseat of a Jaguar. The car pulled off leaving Armani standing in the middle of traffic, suddenly an oncoming Beemer screeched to a halt, he'd almost lost his target. The Jaguar stopped at a red light about a block away. Opportunity was knocking a second time. In this business, that's like Christmas coming twice per year.

Rule #2, always wait for the right opportunity it will come. The light turned green, he hopped on the back of a passing delivery truck trying to make up for lost distance between him and his target. The

Jaguar was now in the opposite lane that had temporarily slowed. It was now or never. He reached for his burner as the truck pulled alongside the Jaguar he released his grip and soared through the air like a bat. The chauffeur's eyes widened with shock but it was too late, Armani's gun was already blazing. The windshield shattered, tires squealed and traffic came to a halt. He yanked he dead man out of the car and shot his partner nine times in his chest before he could get off his first round. Now it was one on one. Him and Ras Silk, his intended target.

No anger, no remorse, no pity, just duty. Rule #4, kill them and kill them quick. Click-click-click. Armani's burner had exhausted its flame. Now the tables had turned. Rule #1 Kill or be killed. Mark Kerr, December 29, 1978 – March 17, 1998, R.I.P. That was the only time that they saw Blade cry, exactly nine days later there was an unidentified body found hanging on the Walt Whitman Bridge. It was believed to be that of Philadelphia's notorious gang leader. That was when Buju decided to quit smoking and drinking. His mother never forgave him, she cried herself into depression, loosing her youngest child almost drove her crazy. His death changed everything, most of the money they had went to wards paying for his final expenses, and since it affected everyone, all business went on hold until they were able to figure out what their next move would be.

Shabba wanted his money or five kilos back in a hurry and they were unable to provide neither of the two. David might have saved him from possibly life in prison, but he did not mix gratitude with business and made it clear that he would not think twice about sending him to hell. Since David was now working for him, he gave him a two-month deadline to come up with two hundred thousand dollars, that was the total cost plus accumulated interest. Besides being the Don dadda of the drug game, he also had what he called the neighbor hood store protection program, all stores in the area had to pay a weekly fee for protection from gangs in and around the area that frequently robbed them. David had no possible answer for his debt, and since it was an effort to help his crew, they all sat down to discuss possible solutions.

Industry came up with an answer that only he could think of. After they carefully studied his theory, all decided it was worth a try. The plan had to be carried out with exact specifications; the first step was to get some one close enough to Shabba so he could trust that person. Blade was the perfect candidate, not just based on his willingness, but also based on the fact that he was not known to be associated with David. A few days later Blade got a job as one of Shabba's look out. They had a store out of which drugs and guns were being sold; his job was to watch the store from a building across the street. There was one person at one corner selling mixed tapes, another at the other corner acting dumb, and tyrants walking the streets checking parked vehicles for undercover police. They were all lookouts trying to make a dollar from the next bundle, with the block moving twenty or more bundles per day, id say that they all made good money.

If the boss eats, you eat, if the boss gets hungry you starve. All Blade had to do was just sit at the window and make sure traffic was smooth, any suspicious activity had to be reported promptly. Five out of every seven days Shabba was there smoking weed or counting money, and even though he had enough workers to make sure his operation ran smooth, he trusted no one with his bread winner. Once in a while a few freaks would come by and have a little party; Blade soon learned that was his weakness. When the women came to visit him he transformed. Most of the women he partied with did drugs and would get high as soon as they got comfortable. I was told he would get high and drunk then have them sniffing crack off the tip of his dick, that would cause him to have an erection long enough to satisfy all their needs.

After two weeks of being silent, Blade was now allowed to take part in conversations. At the end of the first month he knew all there was to know about him and his operation, everything. From the names of his suppliers, pick up and delivery patterns, to whom in Jamaica was importing the drugs and guns. All Shabba did was talk, Blade said he reminded him of Industry. Within the next week his patience was rewarded. He over heard a phone conversation while Shabba was making a complaint about helping backbiters, ironically David was the person in question. When he got off the phone he asked Blade if he knew David, Blade told him a lie that he was from CT and didn't know that many people in NY, only those he was loyal to. "You always seem to have the right answers I could use a mind like yours in my operations. The questions is, can I trust you?" Blade took out his gun and shot the unsuspecting Richard in his leg. Shabba took out both his guns and told Blade he better have a great reason for shooting him. Sure he did.

Richard frequently reported that he was robbed while carrying the money he picked up at the store, Blade told him that it was all a lie. Him and his cousins were stick up kids and would use the same tired excuse to rip off the people they worked for. Shabba did not ask for an explanation, he just finished what Blade started. The honest truth though, Richard was as loyal as you could find, but Blade had to use that lie to gain his trust. "I have some more information I think you could use. I heard you talking about the kid that owed you some money, sorry for listing to your conversation, but I can take care of him for you. I think I know where he and his friends hang out." He told Blade he would think about it after they got rid of the body and cleaned up the mess, nothing more was said until a few days before David's deadline. He told Blade to get rid of him and he would have a promotion awaiting his return, if he did the job properly. Although he was doing well, by killing David he would have proven his loyalty, if he didn't kill David Shabba would just get someone else to. While Blade was tying to find a way to get rid of him, David had to be doing his regular duty.

He was able to work without pay by collecting the money from the stores Shabba taxed. With all the added percentage credit he had already accumulated, he still had not earned as much as ten thousand dollars. Now his hourglass was almost out of sand and that ment they had an even bigger problem. After killing David, Blade was to bring him visual evidence of the murder later that night at a party he was having at his house. After paying a short visit to Diamond who you will later meet, they met at a park next to the school they once attended to start their master illusion. Industry used some red paint to decorate David lying on the floor beside a car with a few bullet holes with a gun in his hand. Buju had a Polaroid camera he used to capture memorable moments with his girl, which would provide the evidence that David was actually dead.

19

The scene looked as real as a body left in murder scene could; now only time could tell. Blade called Shabba to confirm he had accomplished the mission but there was a slight change of plans, he wanted to see the body for him self.

"Good, good job. Bring some of your friends and come to the party, hide the body carefully and I will come to see it later, but for now just come and party with us, I have some people I want you to meet."

Blade called Diamond to know if she had done what he had asked her to do and she confirmed that she already had it covered. When he got to the party he was greeted with open arms and a bottle of Moet. "So where are your friends? Don't tell me that you don't have any friends, anyway, just have fun and later we talk business."

Blade looked around as he quickly scanned the room then placed his focus on Shabba and told him not to worry his friends would soon be there. Blade pretended to be having a great time, he had to, Shabba may have been known to let loose while enjoying himself, but all natural born killers stay focused no matter what. Staying alive is hard work, if the person that died yesterday lost his or her life so easily, imagine being a don or even just a thug. From time to time Shabba would come by and ask him if he was having fun and where were his friends, Blade told him that they were coming from Hartford and would probably be there soon. As the night went by he became occupied by more important matters. For instance the two women he had never seen before treating him like a pimp likes to be treated.

Almost every possible drug dealer with a reputation was there. Blade said that is when he knew he was going to be a don, not just any don that will be talked about for a few months after God has called him home, but a don that will live in the hearts of people for years to come. He wanted to be remembered in a way that we all remember Al Pachino in Scarface or the Godfather, but not make the mistakes they did. In the movie he died, but the respect we have for the life and legacy he portrayed allows us to talk about him as if he were still alive and we are awaiting the sequel. By four am the party was almost over with only five people remaining, Blade, the host, two women and Kurupt. Shabba came down stairs with the two women and a very satisfactory look on his face then he spoke to Blade with a little sarcasm.

"I can see you have friends you can depend on, good thing you have friends like me."

Blade then told him that his friends just arrived and were waiting for him outside, Shabba insisted that he invited them in. Blade returned with Industry and Buju, all guns blazing, Kurupt got more than nine shots in his chest, he was Shabbas' right hand man / partner in crime and none of them expected it. Shabba tried to run up the steps, but David already began to tear his knees apart with shots, as his helpless body struggled to reach the top of the steps, the pain and cocaine the ladies had put in his drink made it impossible for him to go any further. Soon he had no choice but to let go. As his crippled body rolled down to the last step, he was looking David dead in his face, then with his last breath, he told David to go suck his mother.

"Yeah, well you suck this."

David put the Desert Eagle in his mouth and blew his head off. The two women Diamond had sent were still crying and screaming, luckily the music was still blasting and did not allow them to be heard by the neighbors. Industry set his house on fire just to be extra cautious and not leave any marks. They drove all the way to the Bronx and still had no answer as to what they were going to do with the four bodies, they had to kill the whores too, how could they leave witnesses? They had collectively committed their second murder, that way, if push came to shove, they all would be guilty and would not have left an innocent to convict the guilty. Trust had not been a problem among them until Spoon Head messed up. Who is Spoon Head?

He was another Jamaican that went to school with them and was the first person they killed. He was about the same age as Blade is or maybe older. His problem was that he was a thief. After their first robbery they needed a better getaway driver, Rice was too slow and too nervous at the wheels. He knew the streets much better than any of them so he got a percentage. One night after one of their more satisfying moves, Blade realized something was wrong. The rule was this, anything found in a room was yours to keep, anything stolen was shared equally, if it was jewelry, it was sold to their contracted jeweler and the profit split. They came back to the crib and he was suddenly in a hurry to leave, he got up before the money was counted and said he had a very important matter to attend to. There is nothing more important to a thief than knowing how much he is getting from the pot. As soon as he got to the door Garrett reminded him that he was leaving without his keys, he turned around and a Rolex fell out his pocket along with two gold chains.

They said he was taken to the basement and they all stabbed him to death. That was their first official crime, from that day on they thought that they had a bond that could never have been broken. The Rock had a very strict rule when it came to stealing from each other and he was the first to break the rule. They gave no second chance when rules are broken, if you cannot play by the rules, then do not play the game. Back to their situation at hand. What the hell were they going to do with the bodies? They thought of dumping them at the beach, but that would not work, there were cops everywhere. They got to Manhattan and two blocks away was a roadblock. David told Rice to make the left turn and stop half way down the block that's how Blade met Mr. Eastwood.

He was one of the storeowners money was being collected from, not only that, but the kid Shabba had killed at the store was related to him. At first he was speechless because he did not have the money and thought he was going to die. He began to offer David all sorts of stuff so he could get an extended deadline in order to accumulate the funds.

"I am not here to collect any more money from you, I have someone I want you to meet."

That made matters worst, when Blade walked in the room he was almost on his knees. The old man began telling Blade that he had kids and did not want to die, then he went on talking about the value of life and how age is a privilege that has been denied to many and he did not want to loose that privilege. He went on and on and on until Blade spoke.

"Look, we are not here to collect any money for Shabba and you're not going to die, all I want is for you to do me a favor. I have something to dispose of and I need your help."

Mr. Eastwood was now somewhat confused. Industry asked Blade why he didn't just get to the point and tell him Shabba was dead, Mr. Eastwood heard what he said and interrupted their conversation.

"Young man do not play with my feelings, I would do anything to see that rotten son of a bitch dead."

Industry and his questions.

"I could swear you are a pastor, so how comes you use the word bitch?"

Before he had a chance to answer the question, Blade told him to be careful what he is wishing for because he just might get it.

"Just might get what, you just told me you were not going to kill me now your telling me to be careful what I wish for, is this a game?"

Without giving him an answer, Blade sent Rice and Garrett to get the body. Mr. Eastwood was more pleased than surprised to see what was in one of the four huge laundry bags. That became the birth of the Meat shop, no body no crime. A few days later a cell phone rang; it was the phone they took from the glove compartment of Shabbas' car before they sold it. On the other line was the political representative in Jamaica that was doing big business with Shabba. Blade told him not to worry about Shabba now that he is out the picture, but if he wanted to remain in parliament he was to deal directly with him, same business structure, just increased product flow and profit income. Mr. Brown may not have liked what was being said, but he had no choice.

Based on his political interest, I will let the ministry he is involved in remain anonymous. What I can tell you is that he became the voice we needed in high places. He didn't get in politics for what he has now become but at the time he had no choice. He wanted to make a difference and being an honest politician was not the way to do it. He said that he used the profits from the drugs and guns he sold to both support the people who worked for him and to fund what he saw as a way to improve the islands economy. Shabba was just a young gun looking for work, a much more matured young gun. He avoided making mistakes that the recommended guns for hire made. Mr. Brown had made a full proof solution to solve the islands deficit and increase production, and after spending countless hours towards perfecting his plan, it was rejected.

His plan was rejected on the basis that he recommended weed to be legalized and its many medical possibilities utilized. He was also fined two hundred and fifty thousand dollars for presenting such a proposal to the House of Representatives. He did not have the full amount but knew where and how to get it. That's how Shabba got his first job. My name is Sean AKA the "The Brain" I had just returned from Jamaica a few months earlier and had a very impressive portfolio. All I needed was a serious investor, one whom I can trust and was willing to take on some very well structured ideas with high profit margins. I had the ideas but no money at all, so I had to get someone with the same aim as I had and who was willing to go all out on investing.

Life was not ready to let me meet prosperity just yet. For the time being I was being plagued by drama. I used to live in New Jersey with my father. My dad was one of the few Jamaicans who came to the US and did something positive, with out using the help of drugs or guns, he had a 9-5 and a positive mind and is a firm believer in God. He may not always make the right decisions, but he tries his best to make his wrongs right. He once told me that a man can never loose his pride or respect in the streets. If he does, he does not deserve to live in a house. He's my role model, almost like an one-man army, a true general. Salute.

I left NJ due to circumstances way beyond my control. I always saw them at their parties, that's how I met Blade, they always had a party. At that time I didn't associate with them, now I am apart of them.

I was what Blade and I both wanted. Two minds from two different worlds having the same aim. I was a college graduate, young talented and focused. Blade, he attended the H.K.U, Hard Knock University, Street Degree. We learned each others theology and entered the industry. First step, buying a restaurant. Everyone has to eat and everyone enjoys Caribbean cuisine. There was a restaurant going out of business due to the fact that the owner had just lost her husband and did not want to be bothered with continuing her husbands' legacy. It was very big and had a bar in the basement. That later became an after hour gambling spot. The meat shop became a story in itself and one of our most frequent means of disposing our sworn enemies.

We did not own it, but what took place in the meat shop has made it one of my most valid memories. We called the restaurant Caribbean Cafe. The HUD houses were now ready to be rented. I advised Blade to rent them as section eight, that way you get your rent money from the government and eliminate the hassle of hearing ten different reasons why the rent will not be paid this month. Within three months, it was fully operational and profitably taking care of itself. Blade was now at his third level, in order to reach the fourth, he had to enter a different dimension. Shaka Zulu was a mighty warlord. He didn't depend so much on his knowledge, based on the Art of War, but on Black Magic and its powers that protected him.

Priest had promised Blade a blood bath. Which is said to be the ultimate protection. Priest had sold his soul to the devil and was the master of all evil. I remembered one night we were at a concert where Shaggy and Beenie Man were the main acts. Alongside them was Merciless and Elephant Man, they are Jamaica's top entertainers. Priest wanted to get autographs for his daughter and was denied entrance by the backstage security, he obviously didn't know who he was. Priest stabbed him directly in his left eye with his pen. Calm, plain and very simple. Imagine if he'd actually made him upset. Jamaica has a church on almost every corner. All of which belongs to a different denomination. Catholic, Anglican, Baptist, Seventh Day Adventists, just to list a few. In Portland, Blades' grand mother attended what's popularly known on the island as a Revival, Poco or Madda woman church. Blade was forced to attend services whenever he was available or not working.

One could almost say that members of such congregation were involved in some sort of demonic worship, however, don't judge this book by its cover. Priest had a similar such church, so the two were able to relate rituals. Priest was very impressed by his knowledge of what even most people on the island fear, so he took it upon himself to teach him the real meaning of the religion. Just as it is vital to know more about a car than just driving it, the same way Priest thought it was vital to teach Blade that there is more to Revival than just wearing a turban. Before Blade could get his blood bath, he had to make a sacrifice. The body of a 16-year-old virgin was needed. After a long and difficult hunt for such a rare gem, they found their offering in Salt Lake City, Utah. Why the distance? The police would not look as far as the Big Apple for a missing person or orphan. Or will they?

She had a brother who was being too hard headed and who seemingly would cause problems even though he was generously paid. They invited them to NY as he was told she was to be apart of our modeling agency. They sent him to be disposed of at the meat shop.

Back to business. Priest took Blade to a cave, location unknown and not desired to be known. Blade returned with a new look in his eyes after his nine-day ritual had ended. A new fire, evil, deep and desolate. He met with us individually and gave us our own amulets and guard rings. For a very long time they spoke about priest without referring to him directly. Do you know what I mean? For instance David would ask Blade if he is going to see Mr.Mention rather than saying his name or using the alias they gave him. I guess its because I saw them with the different color candles while during their daily routine and told them I did not believe in the supernatural. However, after meeting him, I know that any and every thing is and can be possible.

Now it was time to focus on the more complicated matters, the big dogs.

The restaurant was booming plus the bar alone was making more than two thousand dollars on a bad night. Buju had moved back to Jamaica with Sydonnie and their son Buju Jr., they now had a family and we did not want to jeopardize it. Our appearance also changed, so instead of rocking our usual Fubu, Enyce, Sean John, Rockawear or Timberlands, regular street gear, we now got clean. Felt hats, three-piece suits, gator, and croc shoes, the finer collectibles imported. The secret of America is money and people treat you like you dress. Coke too was selling really fast. We had eliminated major competitors, however a few decided to take it personal. Not only that, but since the NYPD was having difficulty in taking us down, the case was assigned to the FBI. The more money you make, the more problems, so we brought some extra guns. Slime, Rocky and two black Americans, Bugs and Daffy, cartoon niggas with deadly minds.

Slime was one nasty mother-fucker. Whenever we had a problem with a client, Slime would send a message via their wife, kids or closest relative. Young or old, period or not, raw dog.

He'd seen his mother get raped by more than thirteen men. He was only eight years old and was forced to watch. She was also three months pregnant for a man with whom she had a one-night stand. How could she ask a politician with his own wife and kids to stand up to his unborn seed? He was from Trinidad. They migrated when he was eight or ten years old; I don't recall the correct date. What I do recall however is that he told me his mother came home after picking him up from school and found her husband raping his sister. After five years of being married, Miss Palmer thought that she was doing all she was expected to do in and out the bedroom. When was life going to open its doors and shelter her from its hardships? She already lost her first love.

Slimes father was killed during the general elections just days after his birth, now seeing the child she gave birth to after getting raped, being raped almost drove her crazy. How does she deal with finding the man she thought heaven had sent to please and protect her in bed with her daughter? At that time they were living in Tampa Bay Florida, he wanted a new life and moved to Camden NJ. He took his sister with him and she matured into a chicken head, soon she started dancing at a local Go-Go club and ended her life. The Sixers had won the NBA finals and hosted an all star party at the First Union Center in Philly, just maybe a twenty-minute drive after crossing the Ben Franklin Bridge. She was a part of the contract. Luke and his associates got into a nasty brawl with Allan Iverson and suddenly the party became a love nest. Guns introduced bullets to bodies and kissed, sending her spirit to heaven.

For more than seven minutes bullets barked like hungry pit bulls, Tameka was left on stage with ten dollars in her g-string, dead .Two weeks later he moved from Camden to New York.

Rocky was a walking former Jamaican crack head loaded with information. He basically thought that he knew everything. Personally, I think he's still on that shit. No matter how much money he now had to do whatever with, he still looked like a crack head. I guess some people can never change. I still wish he were still alive though. He was from Kingston, very dedicated and reliable, the first and only child of both parents. He was born in 1968, sometime in February, near Valentines Day. He attended Tarrant primary school and passed his common entrance to Calabar high school. For those of you that may not know, the common entrance is a test we take on the island before leaving primary school. There he joined the track and field team under the supervision of one of the islands most respected track legends, coach Michael Clark

"A perfect combination of brains and speed."

a quote from the Sunday Gleaner, the islands leading local news journal. They quoted him after he broke the longest standing track record at the annual high school track and field competition. He clocked 10.12 seconds on the 100m and 45.8 in the 400m. That was during his third year. In the final year of high school he was offered four scholar-ships. He accepted the one to Temple University. In his third year of college his grades started dropping due to his growing popularity. The Pegasus night club in Philly became his favorite spot. That's where he met the woman who destroyed him. She introduced him to a pill called Ecstasy; it introduced itself to the officials after his team broke the 400-meter relay record at the 1990 Penn relays. With his scholarship taken away and threats of being deported, he escaped to the Big Apple.

He got a job with a temp service. That only lasted for half the year. Then he became a telemarketer. In February he filed his income tax and turned to the drug game for luck. He didn't last in the streets for a month. Too many bigger teams of hungrier thugs. He was stuck with most of his dope and instead of listening to the late and grate Biggie; he got high off his own supply. The Rock used to beat him day and night. Not that they gave a fuck what he was doing with his life, he was an educated Jamaican wasting his life on bullshit. David was the one who took him to rehab and took responsibility for him.

Bugs and Daffy were the first two black Americans to join the family. They lived in the Flatbush Projects and sold weed. Nicks and dimes. Their talent was stealing cars. A customer tried to short David on some money and began to get a public beating.

The two were passing by in a stolen car, pulled over and offered D a hand so as not to get any more blood on his Sean John suit. The two were impressive while trying to out do each other. Bugs used a 2x4 wood to hit the victim across the back; Daffy used a 40-ounce bottle of malt liquor to bust her head open.

Even though she seemed half way dead from all that beating, they began using their belts as if she was their child who had done the unthinkable on prom night. Soon the cops came. She was a popularly known crack head so the beating did not really spark much. They did however recover a stolen car. David was impressed, not just by their violent talent, but the info they disclosed on their building that was now up for sale became valuable information. He bailed them and we became friends. There were also other additions too cruel to mention. We needed a bigger outlet and the Flatbush Projects was the perfect venue. Mr. Brown had a few friends in the Mayors office and they assisted us with the necessary paper work.

We called it "Operation Sub-Zero."

A few tenants gave resistance. They believed our business was bad for their building. A few of them joined Ras Silk on the Walt Whitman Bridge. Others had no choice but to comply. It sort of reminded me of New Jack City that was the only time Rice was allowed to play a lead role.

The building had ninety rooms. Only sixty were left occupied. Ten of which were kept for personal purposes. Two of the rooms were transformed into a one room so the kids could have an after school study area. Miss G would have liked that. The first floor had a hall, a huge one. That became party central and after hour gambling spot. In two months all the remanding rooms were occupied. We brought back life to that dump. Fully renovated. Every major holiday we fed the buildings occupants. Their rents were increased by 15% but it was worth it. They now had security, clean hallways, hot and cold water and landlords they could ask for anything and that created after school programs for their kids. Time to put my ideas to work.

# Chapter Three

They had already established themselves as drug dealers, now we were about to become party dealers and everyone wanted to know what was Blade up to. He became listed among those labeled as most wanted, yet he was constantly in the spotlight. Not as a criminal, but as a modern day Robin Hood of the ghetto. The police were having trouble building a case against him that would possibly put an end to his strengthening empire, so the FBI took over. At a time when Blade should be worried, he was the main topic in the entertainment arena hosting a show that highlighted Shabba Ranks, Super Cat, and Buju Banton. The most popular international reggae artist, and the number one hip-hop entertainer, Busta Rhymes. Shyne had been sent to prison after he allegedly took the blame for Puffy on gun charges, so he was not apart of our line-up.

Hot 97 made sure that our show got all the radio publicity it needed. With music by Stone Love, and Adonai being hosted by Jah T the reggae ambassador, it had to be a bashment.

On the day of the event, Flatbush Projects went from housing rags to entertaining riches. Patrons came out in style, carriages ranged from Beemers to Navigators, Lexus to Escalades, with fully loaded entertainment systems, not to mention the Hummers, you name it they drove it. Dress code was fashionably correct. Ladies in their designer evening dresses and suits, something J-Lo, Eve or Halley Berry would be seen in. The men rocked the Steve Harvey and P Diddy baller type attire. Frozen water held its image, everyone iced out. They had more carrots than a vegetarian did, as they popularly say, bling bling. Friends, family and foes all present, a star studded event featuring ghetto divas, ballers and high rollers. The constant sound of Moet popping was like music to the ear, being sold at one hundred a bottle profits to our pockets.

We had ten bottles of Crystal in a wash tub, and a sealed case waiting to be spilled, the best that money can buy. Life was good and at this point easily affordable, music, money, drugs, and whores, I'd say we were in heaven, thug heaven. The performance was as expected, exceptional. Foxy Brown who was promoting her new

31

album, "Broken Silence," also gave the crowd taste of what to expect. All was going great until a club owner that had a little too much to drink flooded his eager with confidence and started acting real dumb. To the extent that he was about to dampen the spirits of all those who seemingly had no intention of leaving our venue until the sun came up and bid them good-morning. They were like vampires and the food, liquor, and entertainment was like blood in purest form.

By 2am, show time had ended for us, in most cases, at any given party; some patrons start acting up after 3am. In this situation, too many hype people, basically in the same profession and who have been drinking. That night proved to be no different. A local club owner popularly known as the "The King" was about to loose his crown, head included.

He'd seen David talking to one of his chicken heads earlier and didn't approve. We were handing out some complimentary gift packages to a few of our guest and he approached us.

"You Jamaicans think that you're the shit, y'all think that you're untouchable? Fuck ya'll." Before he had a chance to end the statement, I had gave him a gun butt in his neck, then all hell broke loose. They had to pass the metal detectors so we knew we were the only ones with guns.

His posse tried to assist, but their efforts proved futile, our soldiers had already covered our unworthy adversaries. King, he was off to the meat shop. The Rev Devon Eastwood operated the meat shop. A 42 year old family man, and father of five girls. He was a very inspirational preacher; one who I personally think took the phrase "eye for an eye" too seriously. Instead of an eye for an eye, he took limb for limb. After I took over all operations, I found out that he was their bookie, since I had all business transactions under control he was now able to focus on his specialty.

There was no mutual connection between us, just a big difference between us paying him five thousand dollars to dispose of dead people and him making five hundred by selling dead animals. A preacher by day and devil by night, sometimes always. He was always wearing shades and carried a bible; looks can indeed deceive the human eyes. Who could tell that a 258lbs man who drives a

1952 Cougar, who doesn't smoke or drink be so cold. The meat shop was conveniently located in downtown Manhattan and that was our intended destination. Mr. Eastwood was about to meet royalty.

We got to the meat shop approximately 4:30am. Mr. Eastwood was already waiting with the equipment up and running. This was my first official visit and we were like kids in a candy store, excited. King had a big mouth and like a real bitch, used it; he uttered something about having a quarter mill in his crib along with a $100,000 necklace he'd bought for his wife. That quarter mill could cover damages to our property, the problem was getting his address.

Rice had the solution, however Slime had an alternative. He took off his majesties robe and tied fishing line to his balls, hook included. Each time he declined to give us information, Slime pulled the line and the hook tore deeper into his testicles. After a few attempts he had almost lost his nuts and we still hadn't broken his code of silence.

Rice decided to try his way. He took a barber razor and began to make tiny slices all over his face. For each time he declined, he got two slices, with the second deeper than the first. After he practically ran out of spaces, he used Jamaican Scotch Bonnet peppers to rub the wounds, mission accomplished, time to dispose of him meat shop style. The procedure was really simple, but could easily upset the stomach of a pig. We put on our overalls and were eager to start. King was already unconscious from his ordeal, probably dead, who cared?

Each body part had to be cut no more than six inches long, so you had to decide what body part you wanted to detach first. We decided hands then legs. Before you chop off his head, you had to put a plastic bag over his upper body so you would avoid making a mess. King had a big head and we had to use a saw to cut his head off and must have broken more than three blades while attempting to do so. I still want to vomit. I could swear I saw him open his eyes when the blade made its way to his knees like paper. To be perfectly honest, I never wanted to have another meat shop experience. I became a vegetarian like David; of course that only lasted for a few weeks.

In fear of what could happen to her after her husbands' mysterious disappearance, Kings wife hired four goons as her bodyguards, rehab crack heads that got out of prison thinking they're supermen because of their muscles.

She still had the necklace and there was supposed to be a quarter mill in the safe. We wanted both and bad. For this operation we used machetes and the blades had been in garlic for a long time and were fully soaked. That way when it chops into your body you feel little or no pain. These were the same types used in Western Jamaica to reap sugar cane. Tun claw. We chopped our way though her guards until we reached the master bedroom. Mrs. Rattery was hiding in her double door closet. She was one beautiful woman. Word on the streets that Omar "King" Rattery had met her in Haiti and bought her from her family due to their economical depression.

Slime had the time of his life. He covered her mouth with duct tape, took her clothes off, and tied her to the bed. Arms and legs tied to each post. If you can't visualize it, I'd recommended glasses. I guess king was too busy being cutie and not doing his duty. To make it more, how should I say, ghetto romantic, he put on a Jagged Edge CD he found in her collection.

Since this was going to be her last sexual encounter, he gave her everything he had. Fucking her as if his life depended on it. While Rice and David searched for the items, I stood guard at the door, just in case. I stood there and watched him force his way into her as he asked her if she was enjoying it. He even told her his name and told her to shout it. Putting passion marks on her neck, kissing her, sucking her breast, he was actually making love, rather than raping her. Then shot her in the head during his climax. He actually emptied his gun on her. Even when she was dead, he was still making sure none of his bodily fluids were being wasted.

I swear to God, I have been around killers most of my life, but never have I seen any as cold as he was. All he used to smoke was weed. It was enough to hide his problems until his problems stop hiding from him. When he realized it was not enough to keep his problems away, he started smoking dope. When he first came to New York, he had met a Jamaican schoolteacher. She had AIDS.

He thought that some one so beautiful could never have something so deadly. AIDS does not care about whom you are or what you are. If you open your life it will come in. Soon he found out that he was infected. That was when he lived in Queens. In fear of being rejected by society, he moved to Brooklyn. He was not very bright and looked like something from the movie Planet of the Apes. Not even the whores wanted to fuck him. He was a getaway driver with a record that spoke for itself, so he got a spot on the team. He was given the perfect opportunity to repay pussy for what one of them did to him. Keep your woman and daughters safe. Don't forget to wear a condom.

After they rounded up the items we left. Slime took her body to be disposed. The necklace was indeed a beautiful and exquisite work of art. Blade put it away for a rainy day. The money was not the amount we thought it was going to be. We only found $150,000. There were also some platinum rings, chain, and earrings, so we liquidated them to compensate for damage to our property.

# Chapter Four

Angel Summers was 5'8"tall, 24-32-36, long black hair and I'd say 138lbs with a degree in criminal law. The Federal Bureau had assigned her to build evidence against the most notorious Jamaican gang since the Shower Posse. At age 25, she was fully equipped with body, brains, and guts. All the right ingredients except the will power to weaken the super charm of the man whom later captivated her heart. Angel had just spent the last few months watching and recording our every move.

While the other members of her task force became disgusted, she became somewhat amused by generosity of the man they now labeled as most wanted and ruthless.

They had raided our scouts a few times, but they were just decoys. Normally, they were caught with a few kilos of coke. That was just to give the agents something for their daily tally sheets. While they were busy practically wasting time on petty busts, we'd set up operation. Our soldiers were making runs across town with 25 kilo of fish scale and bringing the back money unnoticed. We had a system that worked. It's not about working harder, its working smarter. Business was on the up and up. The restaurant was doing so well that it was expanded and added a pool hall. By now, we had a steady $700,000 per month enterprise, including the cocaine profits, real estate, parties, funding small business for a monthly percentage of the profit and most important, doing business with Mr. Brown.

The necklace we had stolen originally belonged to Lavita; an Italian she-devil and the daughter of one of New York City's biggest drug lord, Don DeAngelo, an Italian made man. Even though he couldn't fight his way out of a paper bag, at age 62 he still had the power to eliminate your family without breaking a sweat, just one phone call and it was done. He built a multi-million dollar empire from the ground up. He was like a street hustler, the difference that separated the two was that he dominated a bigger play ground and had a lot more game. He knew everything that went on in the streets around him. He had begun to lose a few loyal clients, including Shabba, and was eager to kill the person causing him so many problems. The same person who had possession of the very valuable item stolen from his daughter.

He sent three of his men who entered the restaurant smelling like Garlic with a message saying that King had stolen a very valuable item that belonged to his daughter and he was very anxious to retrieve it.

Blade sent the necklace to the Don along with King's pinky finger. He'd kept it in preservation as reminder of our first meat shop experience. Although the Don wanted to kill him, he slightly envied him because he saw himself 28 years ago, young, determined, and talented. He had almost begun to admire him. Even though there was no mutual connection between the two, somehow I knew that their paths would soon cross again. For better or for worse, something would happen.

The ad we posted in the local newspaper and the New York Times had begun to attract a lot of prominent business figures from near and far. Even a few celebrities. After what had been one of our busiest lunch hours, we were in the back lot enjoying some weed brought to us straight from Jamaica. Our main chef had a complaint about a customer who was reluctant towards paying his bill. He demanded to see the manager so Blade went to investigate. For the first time he was looking at the man many said had been the maker of John Gotti, Don DeAngelo himself was in the establishment. You could tell his bodyguards had guns from the way their Taylor made suits seemed to bulge. The Don had to come and see for himself exactly what was Blade doing. Most Jamaicans are labled as having very hot tempers and a long history of trigger happiness; of course Blade was no exception.

One could say he was beyond control, I personally watched him pour a gallon of hot oil on a crack head who had tried to steal one of his cars. He was kind at heart but hated to be cheated or stolen from, he would do anything towards being the last man standing, but there is also a time and place for everything. The Don did every possible thing just to see how stupid or intelligent his response would be. He scraped the remainder of his meal on the floor and described it as a laxative, and then he called our chef retarded and said he laughed too much. Then he said the restaurant resembled and reminded him of a shit hole in Mexico, Blade said nothing. Usually anyone who dissed him would have ended up like Nicole Simpson, dead with little motive and no evidence to convict the killer, OJ style, but this time Blade just kept calm. He knew there was something mysterious about him that had brought such a powerful man into his domain. As soon as the Don left we went back to our previous activities, however a few hours later the restaurant was raided by a task force, lead investigator, Angel Summers.

That was the first time they actually met. Who could have ever known that these two opposites would attract, and uptown honey and a thug from the hood? That was my first time going to jail, thanks is to God, within an hour David had us on the street. They only detained us for having weed in our possession. Blade was not ready to leave just yet, so as soon as he got outside the precinct, he stopped a cab and punched the driver in his face with all the cops watching. Back to his cell to begin the relationship that he was already destined for, Blade and Angel, heaven Vs hell, good against evil. When the lawyers were called to come and get him, we went to pick him up, they had confiscated his Lexus for him not having a license.

On our way back Blade sang Beenie Man's Crazy Notion Love.
"This gal walk inna mi life, with a crazy notion of love dat she found, I know she freaky but, no gal can't teck mi stripe, cause out of all the girls, I've been around, I've neva once gone on down, so I'll keep on standing up and stay from off da ground, so could I hear some gun shot inna di air!"

Two cars behind all you hear were gunshots. All our cars have a linked intercom system. That's what we call a fully loaded car. Internet, DVD, and Play station two. Imagine the sound and graphics. If you can't go buy a dime bag of weed and think about it, it will definately open your limited vision. We went to Rice's house to get the remainder of the weed and off we were to see Diamond.

While on our way to Trenton, New Jersey, I dreamed back to memories of being in Jamaica to put an end to domestic violence situation involving a close member of my family, seven months exactly. The first three, I was doing well. I had family, friends and enough money to make everyone happy and yes, money can buy love. No signature needed. The fourth and fifth I went down to what most Jamaicans face on the island, real life, tough life. On the sixth month I had seemingly died, no one cared if I was living, not even the woman I had married. I went to hell and had visions. On the seventh month, I rose; looking dead and all things that would make you think I was on the brick. I met a school principal and she along with a faithful Rasta man, saved me.

Now here I am one of the hottest promoters telling the story of the life in a Mafia I survived.

When we got to Trenton, Diamond turned on the Dancehall music and the party began. The girls that worked at the house Ecstasy were like Hoovers. Sucking on pipes and having the capabilities of a 400 horse power to give that maximum clean. Forget high school sex education, they gave brains, beautiful and dainty looking like something Diamond got from one of Hip-Hops hottest music videos.

Diamond was about 205lbs, 46 years old and by her appearance, you would think she was twenty- three going on twenty-four. Always having a new hairstyle and a hot car with rims. About fifteen years ago she and her daughter was rape by a biker gang in Alabama. Her daughter was tied to the motorcycle and dragged along an old rocky path for about a mile and a half, she died. Diamond herself was raped, but she survived it, however she was forced to have her womb removed because of internal injuries. After watching her only child being raped and then being raped, she decided to become a Madam. I guess that's why she chose her profession. A sick theory, but you'll be amazed to know some of the things that make people tick.

A lot of her customers were from out of town and the things we were told some men say when getting laid would probably amuse you. From personal problems to information that can damaged their syndicate. The number one whore was called Caramel. We called her good times she gave the best service. Some called her Superhead, she gave superhead, with two tongue rings, you always got twice the fun and to bust a nut is always guaranteed. We took good care of those whores. They only knew us as customers and not the Rock.

Buju got married to Sydonnie and both are expecting their second set of twins I think they now operate a supermarket on the island. In respect to his family life, we did not bother to worry him with the details of the current happenings. Knowing him, he'd be back in a minute. He had what we all wanted and we'd hate for him to have a reunion with his younger brother.

Industry wasn't around much anymore. He'd always be gone for days and then returned with info on some current affairs he was involved in. Each time he returned, his involvement became more Donald Trump sized. It seemed as if he wanted to start his own whatever and not be bothered with the family. Most times we just ignored him. He was known for his dramatic stories, so if he told us walk, we would run.

G-Money had now become a #1 Selector. He was on a roll. A party was not a party until the G came through. An entertainment magazine, Globe Times, interviewed him, but failed to publish his biography based on his background. When we visited their office the reporter told us he did not approve of musicians who where involved in drugs or crime. In today's world, music and crime are a couple no matter how you look at the equation. Very few members of the music industry where fortunate enough to get a clean brake. Most entertainers simply have to do what it takes. If he felt that way about G then what would he have said about us? Slime visited him a few days later. Four shots to the head. Local reporter murdered by lone gunman.

Thanksgiving of 2000 was celebrated in a more spiritual manner. We went back to where it all started, Church St in Brooklyn, that was the first place they called home. Instead of having a feast we had fasting. There was a basin filled with the blood of a first born ram goat, that night we were going to sign our contract. Blood in and blood out with no exceptions. If you didn't want to sign your contract you'd just become a soldier and focus on street issues. We had a lot to give thanks for, we were all alive and still had health and strength.

**Prayer of the Dark Angels**

**"BY THE BLOOD OF THE LAMB THE ROCK IS WHAT I
AM.
BLOOD IN, BLOOD OUT. FOREVER SILENT
ETERNALLY DEDICATED.**

**BLOOD IN, BLOOD OUT. THE ROCK FOR LIFE. AMEN"**

# Chapter Five

On New Year's Eve of 2001 we visited the New Testament Church near Howard Beach. It was had been a long time since we all visited church, but tonight there was a natural mystic in the air. Speak of the Devil and she shall appear. Half way into the service a limo pulled up and Lavita entered the holy house.

She seemed to be on a mission. She had that she-devil look in her eyes and her red attire proved no different. After the service ended, she notified Blade that her father requested his presence. This was a very strange request. Italians never get too closely associated with blacks, no matter what the occasion, business or pleasure. Here is one of the most powerful made men in New York sending his only child to fetch what would be looked at as being street scum by other made men.

Blade accepted the invitation while the rest of us went to a block party in Yonkers hosted by Jada Kiss and the Ruff Ryder's. The meeting was held at Mr. DeAngelo's house. Blade told us the place was enormous, befitting the status off a Don. High ceilings clean white walls, white oriental carpeting, and big bay windows that all overlooked Howard Beach. Tasteful and elegant. A fully stocked bar, black leather sofa, old English chairs and a collection of African art. That explained his interest in African Americans, this time Jamaicans. Blade was escorted to the dark room. It was said that very few walked out of that room. They were usually escorted in a body bag.

The floor was covered with plastic, no furniture. The Don entered the room with a loaded shotgun pointed at Blade.

"You've been a real pain in the ass, running around in my town acting like you own it. I would have had you eliminated a long time ago but the pleasure will be mine."

Blade said he held the mouth of the gun and placed it on the center of his forehead.

"I've been dead since birth, so kill me."

Silence prevailed for a few seconds.

"You think you got the balls and guts it takes to run this city? You may have what it takes to run the streets. Let me show you the remainder, besides, there is no fun in killing a man that has no fear of death. Whatever gives you the power to have life and not fear of death makes you a man. You were born of the womb and will live in your tomb."

That was the birth of a new era in the gangster world. Evolution not revolution.

The Don showed Blade that there are rules that govern the world in which they live. The difference between being a ruler and a subject. A more professional approach to the art of gangsters. No more running after people with baseball bats, chopping with machetes, cutting hamstrings, shoot outs or giving their wives a last date with Slime. A phone call or simple e-mail does it all.

For the first time Blade was being given an emotional cross over. A man who has been there and done that was educating a mind that wants to go there and do that. The dons past were to be his future. Probably the most difficult subject matter to absorb was the fact that every thug needs a lady. Not in terms of just sex, but you need to have a place known as home where you can go in and shut the street life out or at least try to. There has to be someone to take your mind from it all and enhance your natural emotional being.

"How can a man who's known nothing but hurt and pain learn to love?"

Blade had never been loved; in fact, the only love he knew was pain. That was something I could relate to. Never been loved .It was either for what they think you are, or what they want you to be. There is always an ulterior motive. That is in most cases. Why?

The Don took Blade to his library and showed him what he was doing at his age.

**New York Times. December 13, 1976**

**Jury Selection to Begin for DeAngelo Trial**

Reputed mob boss Nicky DeAngelo, who has miraculously survived repeated murder attempts, is facing another threat hat could affect the rest of his life. Jury selection is to begin today in the trial of 42 year old alleged leader of the New York Mafia. Federal prosecutors will map out the underworld participants for jurors. After leaving a brutal landscape marked by a grotesque scene of vice, violence and bloody open mob hits. They will try to put an end to his rule of terror. Continuing with Mafia customs, most hits have been accomplished by guns or baseball bats. He has become one of the FBI's most feared mobsters. His restaurant, La Bella Café, became a place where people engaged in extortion, sold drugs, took bets and bought escorts. Two alleged members of the mob will testify against DeAngelo. Those are said to be the prosecutions heavy hitters. Bino Tuscani is the first and the highest-ranking mobster to turn key evidence for the government. The other was Nate Ragazzi. He is a former mob cappo who became an informer in 1975. He is best known for his work as a loan shark. It has been alleged that Ragazzi has received over fifty thousand dollars from the FBI. Attorney Barry Gordon commented that on Ragazzi's deals with the government, stating that it generally affects Nate's credibility. As a result they might not seek the death penalty.

## New York Times April 6, 1977

## Reputed Crime Boss Saved by the Bell

Key witness, Nate Ragazzi, in mob trial was shot dead at a red light just days before he was to testify on behalf of the prosecution. A few hours later brother of NJ native mobster Bino Tusconi died in a car explosion just outside his Elizabeth New Jersey mansion.

## New York Times. May 18, 1977

## Last Man Standing, Gunned Down

Bino Tusconi, 61, was gunned down as he left his Brooklyn home for the infamous trial of mob boss Nicky DeAngelo. Tusconi was the only remaining witness for prosecution. DeAngelo who was facing charges for racketeering, gambling, and loan sharking is also was facing charges for murders which occurred during a mob war. DeAngelo survived several attempts on his life, including the December 26, 1974 saga that wounded him and killed an associate. Lack of evidence is now his savior and will allow him to be released. DeAngelo has been held without bail since his arrest on September 29, 1975. Some observers say frequent prosecutions and internal fighting has left the once "untouchable Mafia," weakened and in disarray.

"This is the last fraction of the NY mob."

A statement from NYC Sheriff Peter Brown.

"However, law enforcement experts say prosecutors can't erase the mob's market for drugs, gambling, prostitution, and other vices. Someone is bound to step in and fill that void. Even thought it's been pounded pretty hard, it would be inaccurate to say the mob is and will be dead. Never count them out."

The rest of that meeting became history. Time to take the business a little more seriously. From time to time, money green Navigator truck could be seen patrolling the restaurant. Each time that same truck passed, no less than ten minutes later the cops would come by for a raid. Seemingly, the driver of the truck was either sending us a warning or setting us up. Either way the mystery driver had to be unveiled. Kevin was a handy man; he could fix almost anything. From giving your engine a tune up to plumbing, that was his 9-5. After six o'clock, he was a hacker. He could access almost any code or system and make any given identity. I'd say he was a computer whiz from birth. We provided him with the plate number from the mystery truck and he provided us with the info.

The truck belonged to Angel Summers. Not much of a surprise. The question was what is she up to?

Blade had a plan. We had a welder make cross bars with spikes that could tear even the best tires apart. Two blocks from the restaurant we had two kids awaiting our signal to lay the bars across the road. The opportunity finally knocked less than a week later. We waited for the right moment then signaled them to lay the bar. Her truck tires were no more. Distressed and pissed, she now needed a hero and Blade became her knight and shining amour. She must have smelled a rat. She threatened to put him in jail for the sabotage of an officer's vehicle. Instead of going to jail, they spent the remainder of the day together. Angel was the type of woman you could look at and fall in love with.

Then once you got to know her, you would want her to become your life long friend. She was a people person, easily likeable.

# Chapter Six

Women, you can't live with them and you can't live without them. Today, love has become a four-letter word. It has almost lost its true meaning. Now it is not about whom you love; it's all about whom loves you. Never the less, you always have to respect and protect your women. They are priceless, at least the good ones. Women come in four categories, your wife, your bitch, a freak, and a whore:

1) Wife: she is the woman you go home to no matter what. The one you awake up to most mornings and go home to most nights. She also has your child, cook your food and make sure your appearance is always fresh and clean. You've been together for a few years now and she has shown you that she deserves to be the queen of your castle. She maintains your home and enhances your natural being. Your wife should be your voice when you can't speak and your strength when you're not strong.

2) Bitch: she is a chicken head with some good qualities. The difference between her and wifey is that wifey has the total package. You don't want to wear your favorite shoe everyday. The heel will get worn down. The bitch is just a reserve kept in the streets. Careful. Never put her before your wife. Home is home.

3) Freak: ready to do whatever, whenever. Every man needs one, most men have one. They put the C in customer service. Unlike your bitch, they just do it to get the job done with no strings attached.

4) Whores: they are the strippers and from what we have found out at the House of Ecstasy, they are stress relievers. Weekend fun. Like ATM's, they are available 24 hours a day. We kept them happy and vice versa.

With all four combined, they make life a bit more bearable and any given moment, fun.

No matter how pretty or intelligent they were, same treatment. We would have a bet to see who could get laid on the first night out with a new face. Most women say they don't give it up on the first night and that is where your skills come in. Who has game from who needs training. No one told lies when the question was asked. Never tell a lie on a woman if you did not have sex with her, if you do then you won't get it.

There is a big difference between love making and fucking. Lovemaking is for home. The slow jams, scented candles and all the good stuff to make her melt. Fuck is duty. Just to bust a nut and release stress. You really don't care if you're called a minute man or not, you just want to bust a nut. It may seem selfish, but it is true. Most Jamaican men are labeled as being crazy and possessive. The fact of the matter is that we are very hardworking men who take care of our women. All we want is our respect. We are a unique set of people and do not like to share the things we treasure. Women, you can't do what a man does and still be a lady. Stick to the script. A man has five women or more and he is labeled as a player.

A woman sleeps with two or more men as she is labeled as a whore. It may not be the fact of the matter, but just be careful how people label you.

Besides being crazy, we are noted to have the good times equipment to make any woman sing like Jill Scott. Never make a woman leave the bedroom unhappy or they will talk. And for those who do it, stop eating them. Women are not restaurants; it's not right. Some women men would die for, even cry for would come by our place and give head to more than four of us. Eight out of every ten women proved to us that most of them could not be trusted, either by choice or circumstance.

Their men would have spent five to six years and sixty percent of his earnings building a relationship. We would spend an hour and play a part in it. When we got the green light, we fucked them as if it were their last day alive. Jay-Z said it all.

"When the Remmy is in the system, ain't no telling when I fuck'em if I dis em, that's what they be yellin' I'm a pimp by blood, not relation, y'all be chasing I replace em uh. Drunk off chris, mammy on E, cant keep her little model hands off me, both high and drunk in the club, singing off key, and I wish I never met her at all."

There is no disrespect towards any woman. If you are true woman I applaud you. If you have a job, have kids and maintain them by yourself, then you're a woman. Just continue to do you. Then again if you've been demoted to chicken head status sorry image is everything and you have to create even a half-decent one for yourself. Face the facts, if a woman loves you, she always will. Don't watch her vagina. If she is going to cheat, you cannot stop it. Again ,women please take note that you can't do what a man does and still be lady. That's the law of nature.

The one thing we love more than women is money. With money, you can always get more women, the more the better less stress. You have to eat all the right foods to keep up, without these foods the body would not be able to function when duty called. For example steamed fish and Water Crackers, Yam, Banana and Dumpling regular. Carrot or Sour Sop juice, Conk soup, Snapper with plenty of Okra, and a six pack of Guinness and a supply of Skunk always on hand will guarantee you will be the king of your bedroom or any location available.

P.S. Women should not be physically abused, unless needed. Some times they do push you to it. Keep in mind that you need them later.

> "Love is a woman
> We were born because of a woman
> This world is a woman
> We got life from God through a woman
> Men should respect all women."

49

# Chapter Seven

Mr. DeAngelo never put his name on anything and he seldom used a telephone, if he did, it was to set a meeting for later. He was a large man, standing 5 ft 9 in tall and weighing over 250lbs. He once told Garrett that he would invite him home so he would eat. He said eating is a very important part of our every day lives, the other important things were women and money. The Don was never in a rush, he knew that people and events would wait for him and like a true Don, it was impossible to surprise him, he seemed to fear nothing. He firmly believed in destiny, living today and death tomorrow. He never carried a gun, I later found out that most times, his wife carried it.

He ran his entire operation in his head, he never wrote anything down, and his moves were almost untraceable.

He was not the smartest kid, or the richest, not even the toughest, his only asset was his talent for violence which was a natural charm, and it fueled him. Braking a leg, cracking a few ribs with a baseball bat, taking off a pinky finger with a pair of pliers or a mid-day public beating was a routine, regular exercise. The Don could corrupt a saint and as he got older and more powerful, most of the charges brought against him were dismissed, either because witnesses failed to appear or mysteriously disappeared. To me, being a wise guy was better than being president. It meant power.

Things became different, more improved and calm. The Don interest had developed into a friendship and soon news of their new friendship spread wide and far. As far as the Dons home land Italy. One night after returning from a stage show in the Bronx, we saw a familiar jeep taken hostage by five punks. The driver was being tied to the door. Rocky recognized their leader, a former crack head he used to share needles with. There crew as called the Notorious Niggaz. We pulled up, they already knew us and respect was given. One of their posse members was arguing with their victim.

"Fuck you bitch!"

He seemed really pissed by whatever she had said.

"Maybe you could fuck me, but your Microsoft needs hardware." One right hand punch and she was out. She had gone too far. Pappy seemed really upset and began mumbling something in Spanish.

Rocky squeezed off a few rounds and their crew disappeared. The woman being robbed was none other than Angel Summers. She must have been coming of duty. We took her to the Bronx where we kept an apartment for unexpected purposes. Robin was kind of our personal doctor. Unlike King's wife, she was one ugly bitch; however, she did have a pair of magic hands to comfort wounds. A few years ago she had a very unfortunate accident. She had been happily married for more than eleven years to the man she thought would forever be her prince charming.

A year and a half ago, shortly after giving birth to her fourth child, her house caught on fire. The baby died in her arms, as there was no way to get away from the furnace. She was burnt from head to toe. In fact, you could see her teeth without her smiling and could no longer grow hair. She was in a coma for twenty-eight days and he never went to see her once. When she returned home from the hospital, the house had been torn down and her husband gone. She was the nurse that helped Buju the night of their first robbery when he got shot. Angel had a fractured jaw from the blow and was very grateful for what we did for her. There is no telling what they would have done to her if we hadn't showed up. Now she had a chance to reveal why she'd been neglecting her job by helping us.

Angel was actually daughter of Miss Guthrie, somewhat a shocking revelation. Her father had left to be with his sweetheart and took their only child. While living in Miami she was unable to contact her mother as her dad withheld all information. She thought the best way to track her mother was to joining the force and utilizes its capabilities. She was able to locate her mother, but she'd already been dead. All she had left was the child her mother basically adopted. He alone could fill he blank spaces and answer the questions that probed her heart about a mother she hardly knew. Blade himself was in disbelief. How could this be happening to him? Seemingly everyone in his life was apart of a puzzle. What next? His mother showing up at his door?

We left the two to sort out and share the memories of a woman they both loved and wished to know in detail. We went to Trenton; I herd Diamond got a few new girls waiting to be sampled by her best customers. Like the Dons friendship, their relationship also blossomed into something special. They had both found what was missing from their individual lives, each other. The love that they both had for one woman, had found itself in each other's heart.

For the next few weeks, they spent unlimited time together. Running around like two kids with absolutely no worries. Then jealously began to raise its ugly head. Lavita also had a crush on Blade, she was a very spoiled rich girl, one who was used to getting anything she wanted. Men usually flung themselves at her, now she was being ignored. To make matters worst, her prize was being taken by someone else. Blade gave up his regular trips to Diamond, quit drinking for a while, and spent very little time at the restaurant. He even missed a few meetings so he could take her to Atlantic City for a week. Now industry was back in town for longer periods of time. Industry always wanted to be the boss; he saw an opportunity and used it.

He started involving some new faces and used his own methods of distribution. After a while, customers became unhappy with the quality of the product a problem we had never encountered. At one point guns were drawn at a meeting. Shit was getting filthy while Blade was still busy being happy. To me, he had found what he wanted, a life, a normal life. In reality the Rock was becoming pebbles.

Lavita seemed to have developed a sudden interest in Industry. I knew those two were up to no good. One night Blade came to my crib, he said he needed to talk. I thought something was wrong at the restaurant but this time it was personal. He said he wanted to get out of the game but it would be very difficult for him. He could survive off what he had, but his crew would have nothing to turn to. As a captain, how do you drop anchor and leave the ship? Blade and I went to see Priest. He met us at the door as if he were expecting us. As soon as we walked in one of his servants tripped and knocked over the fish tank and only three fishes were left alive. Priest said the tank represented us and what had happened to the tank would happen to us and only three of us would survive it. Nothing could be done to stop it, what's written was written.

Then my cell phone rang, it was Rocky. Angel was dead. Someone had planted a bomb in her house, this meant bigger trouble because the first person the feds would want is Blade. Even though he knew that in this game you could never fall in-love, I could see that he was beginning to care for her. He remained silent for a few hours. That night we had a meeting. It had been a while since we had one and this meeting was different. All our meetings were held in David's basement. He had a huge finished basement with a round table suitable for twelve. There was also a bar to accommodate us or whoever he was entertaining and pictures of our island and its flag. Was it too late for him to restore order, or did he really care? Now he wanted us to have a meeting with the Don and ask to join his crime family. It never happened and the police never came for Blade. I guess they wanted to convict him on a much bigger charge, or maybe they did not have enough evidence.

Besides, he was innocent. They might have known that they had been seeing each other but had no real evidence. Someone was either trying to set him up or start him up. The business flow was slightly affected. A month later we got a tip-off on a boat coming from Florida Keys with seventy pounds of pure white.

This could be the answer to our problem, or give us bigger ones. That pure white belonged to a Mexican drug lord known as Mother. She was said to be no ordinary woman. Word on the streets said she did things that made some drug lords look like toy soldiers. She also had unlimited identity and was seen by very few people. She is referred to as a very deadly woman so we did not bother to bite more than we could chew at the moment.

It was time for Blade to make his last transformation to level 5. He moved from his mansion in Brownsville, into a large one bedroom in Queens. Instead of bringing his lavish furniture he'd imported from France, he brought a coffin. A huge metal coffin. He had the walls painted in blood red and hired an artist to decorate the walls with Egyptian writing and signs. He said the writings on the wall are a prayer to the God of death. That was apart of the contract he and Priest had signed. In return for his soul, the devil was to allegedly give him powers over death. Each corner of the room also had a cage with 2 turtledoves and a basin of blood. He also had 2 dogs. Rotweilers. Savage. Not even their master trusted them. Actually he bought three, one snapped at him and he killed it. One shot to the head. I guess the others were fast learners.

His house seemed to be the house of death. Spooky hot and lifeless but that was his temple. The mirror in the ceiling had pages of the bible making a cross. I once asked him about his Temple, his reply, "to be like the devil, you must first live like him."

Psalm 3:5; "I laid me down and slept; I awaked; for the lord sustained me."

Even though they already sold their soul to the devil, they still prayed to God and strongly believed in the teachings of the bible. Don't ask me why, I only pray to God and HIM only.

# Chapter Eight

Each man has his own destiny he is born lives and dies as such. Destiny. The relationship between the Don and Blade had begun to bring in major profits. Along also came lots of very powerful and deadly enemies. Not only with outsiders but also among us. Greed began to show its ugly head. An outside army could never defeat us that easy. Don't get it wrong, a few almost came close, either they didn't have the brains enough to step the paper from growing, or didn't have the guts to get down like DMX in Belly. Always on some Jerry Springer type drama. We fought like Africans using elements and not just guns. I remember a cab driver named Ackbar who tried to cheat some freaks from Long Island on their way to see us.

They found him dead poisoned by the sting of a deadly snake. Infact, I have to feed that Lucifer tonight. Roberto Tusscani was son of a back in the day gangster, not only that, he was now the right hand man of Don DeAngelo. One could say he was in training to become the next Don. His father was killed by a Mob legend; he himself was going to be a legend. That was his personal theory and one he took very seriously. He was only 29 years old and had matured into a very selfish man who was never interested in being a child. While other kids his age were busy with Superman and Nintendo, he was already going with his uncles to shake down cats across town. Now he was a captain in one of, if not the most powerful Mafia.

When teenagers were thinking about sneaking out to smoke Newports or blunts, he was selling ounces of old white whore. Now, he was very eager to be the king of New York. He had ideas that would put New York as the world exclusive # 1 city of terror by far. After the recent attacks, the last thing NY needed was some nut with power abusing it for his own personal pleasure. He was tired of taking directions and orders from the old man. He wanted the spotlight for himself. He knew Tony Wong. A member of the Chinese Mafia who wanted the same things he did. Money- power- respect. Wong represented a syndicate that was ready and willing to do what ever. Don DeAngelo was labeled as one of the most ruthless and deadly druglords of his time, but he had a heart. He knew he had a daughter and grandson in this world. If he decided to join in the bullshit the world would be introduced to a new evil, one that he didn't want his child to meet.

Each of us had a reason to do what we were doing. Wong, I guess he did it because of what he saw happen in his country when he was young. I guess you could say he was driven by images of war and poverty. In order to kill the Don, they now had to eleminate his new found outside friends and their source of existence. In order to eliminate the Dons friend they had to kill their Guard. Priest. To kill the devil you must first become the devil. They knew the powers he had could easily get in the way of what they were planing. They hired a hitman known as Ala. He was also somewhat a young legend. At age twenty-two, he had already killed more people than he'd lived to see years, most of whom had political or religious affiliation.

The origin of his nationally was unknown, judging from his last words, id say he was Italian also. Very few had the privilege to see his face. As good as other hitmen said he was, he had to get some extra needed spiritual items to start his $2 million dollar assignment. They said he got skills like that, so he got paid like that. After a very extensive research, he found that one person who had the power to guide him spiritually. He was none other than Monk. Lord of a demonic church in Haiti. What made him so significant is that Priest was his number1 all time student. Only the mentor could destroy the Protégé. Deep in the countryside of Haiti in the middle of a refuge war, there was Ala getting the last of his 3-day protection bath. A combination of turtledove blood and cat powder made from the bones of freshly killed jet-black cats.

In order to get all the bones, the cat had to be skinned and boiled down to a bowl. The process took an entire day by a wood fire with a furnace that could bring a pot of water seven meters away to a rapid boil. Among a few other things, Ala received a knife. The same knife used to ordain him as a priest. That was the only thing to help kill him. Guns could yes, but a few tried to shoot him and brand new guns backfired. After his visit had ended, Ala flew from Port- au-Prince directly to NY City. Time to send a few people to home sweet hell.

Priest had a vineyard. A place away from home where he operated during the day. Unlike Miss Cleo, he went in dept easily and without the use of cards and the hassle of an 800 number to call and be told a lot of lies. I know I have called them a few times. People came from all over to get things for their spiritual desire. Paying for demonic works of various forms. From keeping their jobs, to getting someone to stay faithful, voodoo dolls for their most hated enemies, guard rings to keep off the supernatural. Anything and everything.

Even lottery numbers. As if he would rather sit and listen to their problems rather than winning a few million.

Ala went in as a member of the day's congregation. As the drums rattled and the members of the church sang those Zion hymns, there seemed to be a different vibe in the air. The drums cried as the wooden sticks released agony while the congregation sang their testimonial.

"I am going to lay down my burden, down by the river side, down by the river side, down by the river side, Im going to lay down my burden, down by the river side Im going to study war no more."

It was now 11:45 am and soon time to sign the midday prayer. A few minutes later the master of ceremonies graced the church with his appearance. Today, instead of reading the first Psalm of David.

He read Psalm 27. Verse 1 & 2. "The lord is my light and my salvation; whom shall I fear? The lord is the strength of my life; of whom shall I be afraid? When evil -doers came upon me and eat up my flesh, even my adversaries and my foes, they stumbled and fell".

He knew today was his last. The amulet Ala had kept him from being able to pinpoint his hunter. A few songs into the midday service a member of the congregation got into spirit and began speaking in tongues. She began circling the seal in the church and started writing ancient language with the chalk. Priest was speechless when he read what was written.

# "HE WHO IS CREATED BY GOD AND HAD BEEN RAISED BY THE DEVIL SHALL DIE LIKE AN ANIMAL. PREPARE TO MEET SATAN."

As soon as he looked at the old woman, she leaped and stabbed him in his head about 14 times. No one was even at least able to get a finger on her. She just crept in and exit. Ala had hit his first target. Monk had sold his favorite student to the worst manner of evil. Money. Priest was laid to rest. June 1, 2001. Blade took him to the same cave they had visited and burned his body. His family was sent to a secret location. However, a few days later they were victims of a car bombing. Who next?

Things were beginning to get very heated. Blade felt as it death was beginning to creep up on him. First Angel now Priest. Then there was Armani's death that still had him feeling guilty. Although the NYPD heard of his death, they didn't even as much as put that yellow Ribbon around the location. I guess they thought of his death as community service. One less scum.

Most Chinese stores are apart of the Chinese Mob. That was just a way of funding their operations. They pay off their depths and import their respective families to join them.

How often do you see a Korean in an old car? Always pushing a tight wipp. You have rarely heard of a Chinese crack head or seen one of them on the corner begging for quarters. Tony Wong's mission was to open a gateway. No rules. Unlimited boundaries. He knew that if he started an all out take over war, they would face too many warlords. Instead of working harder, they worked smarter. If you can't beat them, join them. So he joined Roberto. With these two loose minds on the go, everyone had to be cautious. Including them.

# Chapter Nine

On Sep. 26, 2001 a mega dancehall event called "JUDGEMENT DAY" was held in Jamaica. The event is originally known as Fully Loaded, but due to the recent terrorist attacks on the US by Ossama Bin Ladden, they gave it the name of the day many thought was at hand. His invitation to clash with the best sound systems across the world came from the growth of his fame in the dancehall community. He had been apart of the constant day to day race to be the number 1 dancehall DJ. Now he had the chance to prove himself. The opportunity he was waiting for, infact, it is an opportunity for which every sound system awaits.

It was the biggest event to be held on the island since Sunsplash and Sunfest came about. With a million Jamaican dollars and a trophy worth $25,000. Enforcer from Philly, Stone Love, Hell Razor with Beniton from Queens New York, Mighty Crown, Sound Trooper, The Rock and all Jamaicans leading sound systems. Dancehall patrons came from near and far to enjoy the musical feast. As the sound systems played dub plate after another, it made it seemed even more difficult to decide whom plays tomorrow. The young guns had to take notes. Every possible crew and who of who in the entertainment indusrty on the island were at hand to be judges. The Godfather of Kingston had died recently and they showed respect to him by playing a five-minute segment of songs by almost every possible hit maker. RIP.

At $1000 Jamaican dollars per ticket, thousands came out. Shaggy, Shabba Ranks, Bennie Man, Mr. Vegas, and Bounty killer were just a few of the artist at hand. Tony "Mentally ill" Matteron, Fire Links, Killamanjaro and G.money representing the Rock were the four finalists. By 3:30 am the MX3 entertainment center in Negril Westmoreland was jam-packed.

We knew that they had every possible dub plate, but we had Capleton, Merciless, Bounty Killer, Bling Dawg, Vibes Cartel, Monster Shock and Elephant Man in studio cutting brand new dup plates up until midnight. Rice took a stack of money and told Tony Matteron to match his money dollar for dollar on every tune played.

If the crowd likes the song he plays he gets $100,000 Jamaican dollars, approximately $2000 US. If they like our song he has to pay. Remix after Remix. Combinations he never could imagine. We had the crowd in a trance.

"Hey-hey-hey-hey. Rock-Rock-Rock."

Then on our final dup plate we let him get. A Jay-Z, Bling Dawg, and Lady Saw combination. Gunshots blazed in the air, ladies screamed in ecstasy and thugs popped bottles. We had to play that song more than nine times. G-Money had done it. Kill the ill. Anthony Miller, the host of a local entertainment show, The Entertainment Report, finally gave him the media respect he so long deserved. After the show came the after party. Three days later at the Hilton hotel to celebrate as new King of NY.

I left the party early. I had some personal business to take care of. Garrett had a freak that made it known that she was going to make the now dancehall king feel like royalty. I had no idea of what was about to happen. Her kids' father had just came home from prison. I guess he was unaware of her new profession but somehow found her location. The person at the front desk told us that a man came in and asked for his sister. He told them that their had been an emergency at home and he needed her as soon as possible. They said the next thing they knew they heard two gun shots and later they were taking out Garrett in a body bag. There was no mention of the woman. She must have disappeared before the cops came. We cremated his body and sent it to his family in Jamaica. To be honest, Blade kept the real ashes. I guess now they know the truth.

A few months later we went to Amazura nightclub to find some fresh meat. Friday nights always has some professional women who come out to have fun. Unleash for the weekend. David was on the hunt. He bought a bottle of water and went to interview a face I thought was a little familiar. By the time we were ready to exit, we both had a dime freak and were ready to roll. I had one of those picture perfect women, almost as beautiful as Ashanti is.

David left her in his car and came over to ask me for condoms. He is always asking for condoms, never having a pack for himself. I gave him a few and told him to have fun. He said she is the one that is going to have fun making him have fun as two of her friends were meeting him at his house. I wanted to be apart of the action, but I already had my date drunk from the long- island ice teas. Before he walked away, I saw her get out the car and was walking towards us. That's when I remembered her face. The same girl that was with Garrett the night he got killed. She might have had a little too much to drink because she did not seem to recognize me. I didn't bother to blow the cover. I just sent a 2-way message to Blade telling him to meet me at the meat shop. If my memory serves me correctly, she was the first woman we disposed of at the meat shop.

The Don had a mega plan for NY City. He wanted to build a complex, one that would house an entertainment arena, shopping mall and museum. He didn't think Roberto was ready to deal with that approach. He wanted to put the Italians as forever kingpins by creating a foundation that could only be built on for generations to come. Right now the Chinese has to be the most organized crime family. They kept most of their operations on the down low. You would have to know the streets to know they had a mafia of their own. Makes you think twice before you go order fried rice and not want to pay; they will do more than just spit in your food. Just keep that in mind. When you've ever seen a Chinese/Korean/Vietnamese family in the streets fighting with each other? That's almost never.

They kept any personal dispute to themselves. They would rather be caught in a food store, check cashing, dollar store or a food market catering to their own. Back in the ball game, Industry had just made strike three. A long time customer had made a complaint to Blade out of respect. His pounds were being short by a half-ounce or more. By the code of the streets he should have killed him. Maybe it was out of fear of touching a family member. Out of every pound of coke we sold, he stole an ounce. That's how he supplied his spot it proved he'd been robbing us for along time. David was in charge of making sure the money and product supply was up to date and for a long time he was concerned about the profits. Not that we were not making money, he just thought we should have been making more. He was right; you can never bite the hands that fed you.

61

Industry never played by the rules. His out of town visits had begun to invite strangers into town. One of his personal clients knew one of our present clients and decided to have their scientist compare the product. He was also substituting the pure white with something else.

He was doing great by extending into making his own money; the method he was using was the problem. In the game of drugs you have two choices to begin with. Make some fast money or face twenty-five to life. The coke we had on the streets at that time was called The Great Depression. The crack heads loved it. Most of them judge the coke by the effect it has on them. If it made them vomit, then it was the best. The Depression had killed two of them within hours of being on the street. We had to tell the cook to chopp it up some more and be easy on the secret ingredient we used and changed the name to Hope. I wonder if he is sniffing? Maybe it was just too strong. He could easily get high by it just touching his skin.

You know what, I think I have to start keeping an eye on him. Industry just wanted to have more than he needed, eating an entire bread, when all he needs to be full is one slice. Plain greedy, so we did what was necessary, we took his life. He was apart of us so we did not bother to shoot him or send him to the meat shop, we gave him a chance to face his worst fear, dogs. From all of the sales we made and the ounces robbed he now owed us roughly owed us at least 18 kilos of coke. A debt for which he could easily have paid, and was about to. Not with money, but with his life. We sent Rice to get him. They were close friends and Blade thought both might have been involved. They didn't ask Rice if he was guilty, they just kept an eye on him. If we all went, then he would know something was wrong. They met us at the location we told Rice to take him to. He didn't deny stealing any of it, just the amount he was accused of stealing.

No one wanted to hear what he had to say. Maybe if we were not so accustomed to his lies we would have believed him. He was honest enough to admit, but stupid enough to steal it. We had a cop on our pay roll that had just made a bust on a dogfight ring in the Bronx. He said the ring was run by a group of Mexians who gave the dogs crack in their food to make them fight longer and to be more savage. We sent Rocky to get them. Diamond had already rented an apartment in Staten Island for us to take care of our back stabber. How can you be apart of a syndicate and steal from it? That's like stealing from you isn't it? If he would steal form those he practically grew up with, what would he do to me whom they still basically hardly knew? We bought some fresh meat and made Diamond rub it all over his body, this way the pits would have a bigger appetite. She didn't like him that much anyway. He had unpaid pussy bill at the house. We took him down to the basement and let in the dogs through the basement door. Industry had gained a few pounds, in-fact; you could call him a fat boy.

He was about to say something and I kicked him down the steps. Those dogs did him dirty. Death before dishonor. Having a thief in the family was worst than having an unidentified hit man on the loose. He always wanted to be a star and now he was. South Jersey's Courier Post had a front-page article about an unidentified body found in an empty apartment. Sources say the body was beyond recognition, as 3 pitbulls were still munching on the body at the time it was found. Two of the dogs had broken necks. I guess he died fighting.

The Don said he had some very important business he wanted to discuss and his daughter delivered the message along with a plea for Blade to be cautious. I guess she really might have had a genuine feeling for him. The meeting was held at a fund raising dinner I organized. I used to teach at an all-age school in Jamaica and since I was in the position to help, I decided to have the event, just a small token towards community development. Somehow I had a gut feeling our mystery friend might show up, so we were prepared, I hope. During dinner, the Don said he knew what was going on and exactly who was responsible, but like a real don, he has to allow destiny to take its course. Dons have to die so dons can be born. He was most entertaining. He told us stories of his past and how being a kid watching the old legends taking care of business was fun. Giving us his most vivid childhood memories as if they happened yesterday. His father was a construction worker and his mother was a housewife, one of the best cooks he had ever known.

If that was my mother I would say the same thing, but any way, you would never tell such a kind looking grand pop was on the FBI's list of most wanted.

Even though he could have put a stop to all what was going on, he didn't. When I was young, I asked my mother what would I be. She said no one can tell the future, you can only do things to build one, not but there is still no garantee of it. We were about to make a toast "Here is to life, money, power and" … blam! The Don was dead. A bullet left a hole the size of a bagel in the back of his head. I was right, Ala did show up.

"Sean shut it down because a pussy dead tonight!"

Suddenly bodies began to fall across the room simultaneously as gunshots whistled the tune of death. Blade got shot in his left arm and that's when I spotted our problem.

He was about 5ft 10in, approximately. 165lbs, with cornrows and light skinned. This time he was dressed as a waiter. I signaled D to cover Blade and hit the power switch. Lights out. His mistake was having a red light on his gun. We were both shooting at each other from difficult angles, so none of us made a hit. He was trying to make it to the exit and I was determined not to make him get out alive.

Clip after clip shells fell all over leaving only a tiny smoke and their victims' dead. Finally we were both face to face. I knew my gun was empty, but you can never make them see you sweat. Rule number 11. Always keep one in the chamber for the next person or you. He took off his shades and that's when I realized that he had only one eye. He said nothing. I was a good talker. My mother once told me I was capable of talking my way out of any situation; this time I did not break the silence. Only the dead spoke. Looking each other in the eye with only one thought in my mind, trying to recall if I might have one left in the chamber then boom. The motherfucker squeezed one in my chest. I did not bother to hesitate to make my move. I just dropped on the ground as if I were dead, mamma ain't raise no fool. I guess it was too dark for him to search for any other targets as he made his way across the room towards the exit.

Stepping on dead bodies and killing anyone that moved. As he reached out his hand to open the door, like magic, it opened and he was looking down the barrel of a 12 gauge shot gun. Boom- Boom-Boom, three shots in his belly. Then he began saying something in a foreign language; Rice shoved the gun in his mouth and almost took his head off. Big guns really do make a big mess.

Was I lucky? I don't think so, you don't stay alive in this game by being lucky, people stay alive by being cautious, smart and having an extra clip. Like condoms, I always wear a vest. Never get burnt by a nasty woman or a nigga with a burner. That's why I always shoot for the head, so niggaz don't come back to haunt you like Freddy.

To me, each person's life is like a movie and we are not rewarded with a sequel. You have to live your life to the fullest and never be afraid to make your dreams a reality. Remember age is a privilege denied to many. Blade was not hit that bad, but he did need some medical attention. Robin could easily take care of him.

We had to burn down the restaurant. We caught a few cats soaked them with gas set them on fire and let them run in the restaurant. We had to. The place was destroyed. Bullet holes, dead bodies and not much chance of ever convincing our customers to return. The police were already closing in on us and to make matters worst, we had an Italian kingpin dead in there. We fabricated a story and told the police that we had been robbed and that the gunmen had killed a few innocent people. As for the fire, we blamed the stray shots that hit the gas tanks and caught the place on fire. Our accountant told us the best thing to do was to put the insurance money to work on the stock market. Since prisons shares were making money, that's where the investments were made, that way we would still have that extra income.

The police commissioner told us that he personally would be keeping an eye on us.

Our accountant was a single mother who killed her only child by mistake at her home in Jamaica.

I guess that on that particular day she was just tired of fighting hard times. Not necessarily money. She had just lost the man of her dreams. They had been together for two years and she got pregnant. He introduced her to life. Took her from poverty, cleaned her up and gave her all he could and more. Then he left for the USA. She had lost her virginity and got his heart in exchange. As a part of his plans for their future, he went to study economics at a Business College in New York. All was well. They kept each other updated via letters, Western Union and e-mail. That's how they grew with each other. It created an unhealthy relationship but what other choice did they have? Until he found out she was fucking a few other people on the island. All the years they were together he never cheated on her. Now she had betrayed him. She herself confessed to her big mouth cousin that she once fucked his best friend. He always thought about it but when you love someone you try to deny the fact they may cheat on you. So did he.

He graduated in the top 20 students and was offered an office on floor 53of the World Trade Center. He had only been there for 4 months. His benefits had just started to kick in and he began making enough money to feed his family properly. On September 11, 2001 he, along with more than 6000 innocent and unsuspected people lost their lives. Where were you on Sept. 11?

Words still fail to describe the unbelievable tragedy. The devastation of that terrible day. At 8:45 am a plane hijacked by terrorists crashed into the north tower of the World Trade Center and minutes later another into the south Tower. A moment of history for New York as those who watched helplessly as one after another, the 110-story twin collapsed on the heads of rescue workers, firemen and police officers. In a matter of moments, thousands of lives had been lost, including the king of her heart. Back home in Jamaica, she was only one of many mourning their loss. The two had a child who at that moment had the flu. She was just trying to give him the medicine. As she held him in her lap, she closed his nose so he would swallow. Her mourning heart drifted into the passion of missing the one it loves. Wishing heaven would send back the only gift it knew. The baby was already dead when reality awakened her. In less than a week she had lost both men in her life.

We needed a new accountant and she had the qualifications.

Priest and his family was killed, but later we found out that there was still one child alive, her name was Tavina. She was away in college, or was it grad school? Wherever she was, she was still alive.

I never found out how she knew about her family, all I know is that she was maybe 5' 9', maybe 148 lbs, thick, beautiful girl in jeans and tims looking for revenge of whoever had killed her family. A family she was trying to make proud of her by doing the right thing. Now she was back in town after her fathers' death. She was studying to become a biochemist. She could invent anything, that's anything that had to do with a bomb. At a time like this she could become a very valid asset. We needed any thing and anyone we could trust. In fact, we needed a miracle, fast. Ring- ring- ring. Blades cell phone rang. It was Buju.

"I know what's going on and you can't win. Come to Jamaica, I have someone that may have the extra help you might need if you are ever going to have a chance in this war. I will set up the meeting, the flight leaves in three days."

# Chapter Ten

After our mystery call, Blade was left in Total confusion. Who in Jamaica could have the power to help us and why did Buju call after all this time? How the hell did he get his number? Even worst. Inviting him to Jamaica. A meeting was called immediately. Kevin, Rocky, Rice, D, Slime Mr. Eastwod Tavina Buggs Daffy and me.

After Blade had related what the Buju had stated, mixed responses began. David did not have much to say as usual. Rice thought it was a good idea, me, I think we could use the vacation. Besides I missed my kids.

When all was said and done, Blade had to make the final decision. We had Kevin make up some fake passports and call Air Jamaica to confirm the tickets, just in case. We only called Mr. Brown to confirm shipments, but this time we needed him to check into the matter and make sure it was somewhat legit. If he found any information on the plane tickets, then that would mean big trouble. Why? If someone was making reservations for you to take a flight with fake identity and someone in politics is able to track your flight information, I guess you might as well plan to be escorted to jail upon arrival. Securities at the airports were now tougher than usual after the sky jacking of a commercial airline by terrorist. Now sky marshals were now put on flights, no more passing of a few dollars to hide your objects, customs got airtight. We had to make sure the identities were full proof. Slime's only contribution was to go see Diamond.

When we got there she greeted us with open arms. Not necessarily because she missed us, we always paid for the platinum package. A thousand dollars and the house was ours for four hours. Not to mention the big tips we gave the ladies. Industry never tipped the girls, his idea of a tip was to give them a note.

"Brush your teeth after you give a blow job."

Diamond told Blade that she had a dream about us going to Jamaica. No one said anything to her about what had happened. Things just became even more mysterious. First the call then a dream. That night we must have had too much to drink. We woke up in a whorehouse. The next day I got a call from Blade, I was to be at the J.F.K airport in two hours with no luggage.

When I got to the airport Blade said he had a vision from Priest the previous night. A long time ago, Priest had told Blade that he would be faced to make a decision that will either lead us to destruction or victory.

"What do we have to loose? If we go to Jamaica and they try anything, all we do is leave behind a few soldiers that could come to Jamaica and set them straight, besides, we have one of the most powerful person on politics in our pocket. We have been funding his constituency for the past God knows how long, if anything happens to us, he goes down. I don't think he would risk that happening. Then again, we could get the help we needed to size up to our competition".

For the first time since drifting across the Caribbean Sea on a banana boat, Blade was on his way to an island of which he only had distant memories. The stories he heard of his mother before her tragic death, his granny, cousins with whom he used to play, memories of a vague past now occupied his mind.

"Please fasten your seat belts and put you trays back to their original position".

I swear to God, that hostess is the true definition of fine. As the plane approached the city of Montego Bay, you could see the rich green hillside of Western Jamaica. The long strech of white sand beaches lined with hotels and resorts. It was like going to paradise all over again. Beautiful Jamaica. The island that most people come to relax and enjoy our hospitality. As soon as they leave our island, we are once again labeled as violent drug dealers, at least many of us.

Most Jamaicans come to the USA, work 2 or 3 jobs so they can be able to make life a bit more bearable for those back home, then they say we have taken the opportunities that they fail to utilize.

"I love America. It is the only place on this earth where you can go to sleep broke and wake up a millionaire. Yet there is no place like home."

He had graduated from boat to plane that's what I call travel by air and sea.

When we got through customs for having no luggage, we were approached by a female who verified our given identities and took us to our first destination. The Point Village hotel. That's where we met Prince. Our Mystery friend that Buju had told us about was about 6ft 2in, 190 lbs. and as young as we were. Age has nothing to do with having money or power. Money and Power comes with how quickly an individual is able to utilize life's capabilities. Prince as they say had the city lock. Keys in his pocket. He tried to assure us that he was friend not foe. Prince had been hearing stories about us and all that we were doing. Making money from almost anything. He said he respected Blade for having a millennium Midas touch that turns business opportunities into platinum profits.

Him and Buju had become friends via business. He also knew about the past killing of Don DeAngelo, but not the full extent. However, he knew that we were going to face combat just for being associated with him.

Prince told Blade that we were forgetting to do the most important thing. Have fun. Outside our individual rooms there were some of the most beautiful women that our island had to offer. We call it the wickedest slam. Close your eyes and just imagine two women with the perfect ass, breasts as hard as the sun on leather. Thick lips that grip like nothing you've ever felt. Not only tight, but also they ride with moves only a Jamaican dancehall queen could possess. No matter what other women of different nationalities can do, by far the Jamaican women are the best in every way, big up and nuff respect.

The girls I had made a setting that still brings a smile to my face every time the memory surfaces. First both women gave me a bath. Then while the first woman was applying the body lotion. The other got busy on my little solider. She used the juices extracted from the fruit of my choice (sugar cane) Instead of the usual emotion lotion used by most women I know. With her mouth and talents, I have to say that was my number one experience to date. When a girl is that good, not one but both of them, the sex is and can only be described as incredible.

I took a day by myself to reflect on my life and the seemingly dark direction it was headed in. I used to live in Camden NJ before moving to NY. Two years ago I went home to visit my family. My sister and I were like each other's best friends. She told me that she was raped one night after leaving a concert by a cab driver. She was scared to tell the police as he told her he would kill her. Being afraid of what people might think of her and the shame it would bring on the family, she remained silent until now. I told her not to worry and took her to the doctor to get a check up and by the grace of God she was fine.

I was only there for a two-week visit so I waited for my last day to take revenge. He did not know me so it made my plan much easier. I had a friend of mine pay him to take me to the airport. From our location to Montego Bay it takes almost two hours. I usually give the clothes I take to the island to the less fortunate so I had only hand luggage. We stopped at my mothers' house for some fried fish and bammy that she had prepared for me, that is what I told him. The house really belonged to my sister. I invited him in and locked the door then she came out. In an instant there was a very funny smell in the house, the cab driver had shitted himself. You should see a grown man cry like a baby, telling her how sorry he was and that he would pay her. I hit him with the first thing that I could find, a pot on the stove. Then my sister came out of nowhere and started chopping him.

She seemed to be in a zone as her hand directed the cutlass to different parts of his body, then his risk fell off and she was still chopping. His white shirt had now become red, he was dead and she was still chopping. I had to pull her off him. When we got done I burnt the house down. As you can see, I am in the habit of burning things. She moved to Kingston and later became a stripper. A few months later my mother called and told me she hung herself, I miss you sis. I left work that night and went to buy some weed, just so a dark day would seem a little brighter, that was just not my day.

I always bought weed from the Africans in Camden, they always had some good weed. They were in operation for a very long time and I guess the local police were tired of them. I would not go as far as to say we were friends, but on a good day I would chill and smoke a blunt or three with them. That particular day I had just been told that my girl was pregnant. Well not really my girl, just a few nightstands. We were just chilling when a crack head came up to us and asked if we had ready. They told her to get away and she started cussing the world. Drama. Listening to a crack head argue can be very amusing, so we enjoyed the free entertainment. At least they did. I looked across the parking lot and saw a car with the lights off creeping towards us. Then I saw two cars coming up the one way street, the dogs started barking, and before we knew what was happening, it was police every where. Prison or jail was not on my agenda at that time, so I did the first thing that came to mind. Run.

I did not have a car while living in NJ so I had to either walk or take the bus. I guess the exercise was paying off. I was speeding enough to get a ticket, that's if the pack of fat fools chasing me could ever catch me. I got to Cousins supermarket and almost slowed down, that is when I realized two cops were still running after me. I was almost mid winter and my First Down jacket was holding me back. I managed to get it off somehow and changed gear. Then I got to a gas station and saw an old woman putting air in her tires, I jumped in her car and hit the turnpike. Next stop? New York City.

Blade wanted to visit Portland. The parish he once knew as home. He told me that while on the plane the memories of his not very delightful past made him want to kill those responsible for the death of his mother. Some how he had hopes of finding a man named Joker. He didn't know him, but he knew his name. Blade was not very good with names, but he was the man they told him was responsible. I told him it would not be a good idea to. At least not until we took care of our unfinished business overseas. For the next couple of days we just enjoyed the great service offered by our hotel and the exceptional beauty of Western Jamaica. In our second week on the island, Prince took us to Kingston and introduced us to his crew. Blade had taken a large amount of money for Mr Brown so he could meet the politician that made big things happen for us. Their very breif meeting was held at a Catholic church located in down town Kingston so as not to draw any unnecessary attention.

Keep in mind that if you show me your company I can tell you who you are.

Kingston is a world within itself. A combination of Miami, California and New York mixed with the best of what our island has to offer. Americans say it's off da hook. We say Bashment. Everyone is his or her individual model on a runway. Name brand and only. If you want to know the cars driven by the L.O.Y's, (Lords of Yard), picture the cash money millionaires. All limos had rims, very expensive dubs. We got to Kingston on a Saturday night and he took us to Assylum nightclub in New Kingston, uptown. Each patron made an entrance. Ladies looked like angels without wings. Have you ever seen a woman with a million-dollar body and food stamps face or vice versa? We saw the picture perfect beauties.

Diamond stayed home. I guess she was still in total shock from the fact that at her age a young Jamaican man could shift her womb. She herself gave him five thousand dollars for the greatest sex she ever had. Like Stella did, she's taking her Winston back to the U.S.

At midnight the club was already packed and doors closed. We waited awhile to see how the big balers on the island did their shit and then showed them…Some crews bought cases of Heineken, Guinness a few bottles of Alize / Moet or Henny. We bought five buckets of Moet. Each bucket had seven bottles and five bottles of Crystal and a shot of thug passion for the house. By 4 am, we had Shattas (Jamaican Notorious motherfuckers) who wanted to make sure we were protected. Rule number thirty, be friends with the devil, never trust him.

We spent the Sunday at a fish and bammy fest at the Boston Beach in Portland. That's the closest Blade got to home. Boston Beach is most popular for its Roast fish, jerk chicken, jerk pork, fish tea soup, festival, and most importantly, bammy. It was beginning to turn out to be a great day for relaxation until the sound system selector announced the arrival of the Hot Roses crew. They pulled up on high powered bikes and four of them came out of an Escalade.

There must have been about fourteen of them, dressed to the bone and spending money like they just won the lottery. At approximately five o'clock a young lady was walking by us crying with her face swollen. I asked her what had happened, but she ignored my concern. Blade stepped to her and asked if there was anything he could do to bring a smile to a crying angel. She smiled. Then they both walked back to where we were. After being introduced to us, she began to tell us what, or rather who made her upset on such a beautiful day.

Her babies' father who constantly abused her. Then she mentioned his name. Joker!

"Who? What did you say his name was?"

I looked at Blade and you could see the changed expression on his face. Then I recalled the name he had mentioned to me earlier. Then he smiled. I knew he was thinking dark thoughts. Very dark thoughts. He told her he wished that everything would work out in her best interest and went to ask Prince a few questions. When he asked Prince about Joker, he told him he used to be a small time thief who smuggled a few kilos of coke to England and made it big. He had moved from St James to Kingston as a kid and was influenced by his elders to go on robbing sprees. Blade said nothing. I went to the bus we had rented to get some insect spray and saw the same damsel once more in distress. This time she wanted to get home. I called a taxi and paid the driver to take her home and told him to come back so he could take me home. I told Blade that he should just walk to the exit in an hour without being noticed. Then I told David that he should call me at exactly ten pm.

When the taxi came back at approximately eight o'clock, I told him that my girl had left the beach with my house keys and he should take me to her house. They lived in Harbour View. Almost an hour from where we were. We got to the house and told him to meet us at the drive in at exactly fifteen minutes before ten. That way if he was late, we could tell David to come get us when he called. There was no one there so we had to wait. A few minutes later he pulled up in his Escalade; you could hear the music blocks away. As soon as he put his keys in the door to enter the house we had guns at his temple.

"Yu know who yu a fuck with pussy? yu dead already and yu don't even know it, a mi name Joker. Yu, yu father, yu sister, and yu dog dead. Not to mention yu madda"

Blade broke his jaw with one right hand slap from the gun. He fell to the ground and began to plea a bargain.

"Tell mi what yu want? Money? If yu want coke mi have five brick inna mi kitchen."

Blade just stood there looking at him.

"There is only one thing you can give me to let me spare your life".

Before he had a chance to hear what he could exchange, his girl tried to run. As soon as she got on her feet I kicked her. Her period came immediately. Something smelled. Joker had shitted on himself. "Do you remember back in the mid seventies when you killed a pregnant woman in Moore town Portland? That was my mother, and even though I didn't know her, I told her I would someday revenge her death".

He just lay there looking dumb as if the memories of those he had killed were a dream he had as a child. Blade shot him in his leg and suddenly his memory was once more fully functional.

"I didn't know. Fi real I didn't. If I had known that was your mother I would never even rob her. Just give me one chance please".

Blade gave me the gun and told him that he would give him a chance. "If you survive a chop for each year I have had to live without my mother, then I guess you will have that second chance".

The first chop was in his head, the second in his belly, his gut opened like road kill. By the fifteenth chop he was dead. We didn't want to kill his girlfriend. Then again she could be a potential witness. I told her if she ever said anything to anyone, I would personally come for her myself and introduce her to Slime. When she asked who was Slime, I told her the worst dream she could ever imagine. A dream she did not want to become a reality. Blade gave her half the money we found and told her to enjoy her freedom. We took the coke and gave it to Prince. The remainder of the money was kept for something else.

It was during the final weeks of August and the back to school rush was on. Unfortunately, not all the parents were able to keep up with the high cost of funding a family of anywhere between two to six kids; we went to downtown Kingston one afternoon, just to chill, white tank tops and shorts, no bling-bling. If a thief in Kingston wants your ring and can't get it off fast enough please be 100% assured that he will cut that finger off, no joke. We entered a store, Costco. A mother of five was asking the manger for a discount on the school supplies she'd bought. She laid all her cards on the table and was desperately trying to explain that she was a single mom trying to make two ends meet. He turned a deaf ear to her.

Blade stepped to him and after saying what ever he did all the cashiers closed their windows. The manager went on his intercom and ordered his employees to issue school supplies free of cost. Blade had told the manager to give the item and he'd pay. The money we got from Joker was used to pay for the school supplies. The island is filled with investment opportunities and natural resources that our blind government is yet to utilize. Prime example Herb AKA Ganja / weed. Natural grown weed in parts of Western Jamaica example Orange Hill will give you a natural high just by walking through the field. With all its natural talents and usage doctors have discovered, if legalized, I'm sure export opportunities would become infinite. In the time being farmers keep up the great job. Speaking of farmers, I think the government really needs to put much more effort in giving as much assistance to them as possible. Instead of importing so much food, give them the financial backing they need to produce what we eat. Anyway, that's an issue by itself. From deep sea fishing in Negril, hiking in the Blue Mountains in St. Andrews, horse racing in Portmore's Caymanas Park, and to top it all off, clubbing at Asylum night club. Despite our economic struggle and high crime rate, I would never give up my nationality or deny I was born in the greatest place on earth. Jamaica is indeed the island of paradise. We all vowed that if we made it through this war, we would go back home and make some serious investments.

Prince took us to a mini resort deep in the countryside of Clarendon; Diamond stayed at his house in Spanish Town. The resort was like boot camp. All the necessary equipment needed for training was available. Shooting range, modern gym equipment, and a field with army battle features. For an entire week we had cornmeal porridge and intense training. By the sixth day we were all the best shape of our lives and our minds set in killing mode. Take no prisoners. On our final day we jogged ten miles with sacks on our backs filled with twenty pounds of rock. Of course we were rewarded with some picture perfect ladies and fruit juice at the end of our vigorous training.

Jamaica has a justice system like none other. The people took care of crime offenders and the police took care of the bodies, if they found it. The police was called after the method of justice was passed. A girl in Seaview gardens was raped. Home community of international reggae superstar Shabba Ranks and the now king of Dancehall Elephant Man. She was only fourteen years old. The men who raped her sucked her titties until she had breasts. All three men got different treatment. The first was the girls' uncle. They put him in a corner and stoned him to death. Even when he stopped moving, her father took a rock weighing no less than frothy pounds and dropped it in his head. His head burst open like a watermelon and his marrow splashed over his shoes and his blood slowly drained as his fingers trembled as if he was still trying to hold on to his life.

The second was whipped and salted like a runaway slave that was caught. They stripped him and tied him to a light post in the Community Square. The whips were made from the belts taken from left over cable wire. For more then four straight hours members of the community took a chance to whip and salt his wounds. Luck was with him; the police came and took him to the Kingston Public Hospital. One of the nurses on duty was the girl's aunt and she injected him with an empty syringe. If you paid attention in biology class then you know what happened.

The third was giving a similar treatment given to Industry. First, the girl's mother used a knife to cut off his dick, then they tied his hands to his legs and put him in a pigpen with four pigs who were more savage than dogs. I never knew that a pig could tear through human flesh so easily and quickly. No wonder so many people refuse to eat pork.

In another crime related story. A woman was being raped by a freak who demanded the she sucked his dick. After he repeatedly beat her to fulfill his fantasy, she gave him a blowjob he will never forget. The woman bit his dick off completely. Talk about trusting professionals with your valuables. After two years of being together, a man has to rape his woman for pleasure. He should have had all four categories. Never put all your eggs in one basket. The man shot his domestic partner and then himself. It is not really a matter of the police on the island do not care about the citizens concerns, but most people do not feel comfortable to knowing that someone who has interrupted their way of life should sit in jail, with three meals a day, getting fat and soon be realized so they can repeat their act of defiance.

With our minds focused and our bodies in almost perfect shape, we set out to find a woman in Westmoreland who come in very highly recommended. She and Priest shared similar occupation. Good women are hard to find and she was no exception. After an exhausting drive from Kingston we got to a community named Withorn. Neatly located in what seemed to be a cluster of bushes. There laid the beautiful Garden belonging to the Rev. Mother Graham Miller. A 6 ft. Rastafarian woman of class and tremendous spiritual powers. She greeted us in tongues and welcomed us as noble warriors. She gave us the reading of our lives. Diamond came out of her office with tears in her eyes. After an intensive and direct reading she gave us the one thing we needed, a solid prayer. She told us that the power we need we were not with her, but within us. Not to fear our enemies, but let them comfort their worst fears. She also told us that eighty percent of the times, people do not have enough faith in God.

It is not always about some one putting a spell on you. Most times they just need to hear the truth and have some one they can talk to. Powers and principalities do not govern our lives. There is and can never be a greater power than the power of God. She herself, mother of three beautiful kids, is in-fact mother of many.

Not just to those God blessed her womb with, but all those who need a mother, despite race, color or creed. We spent the remainder of the day enjoying the river adjacent to her vineyard, which also hosted a unique collection of birds, animals and flowers. Somewhat a Garden of Eden.

Two out of every ten tourist that visit the islands have sexual intercourse with a native. One out of every fifty leaves behind a child. Prince was apart of the statistics. Like many of other women, she met a sweet talker who gave her promises of a better life and long and lasting love. A Russian Romeo, he kept in-touch, but never returned to see mother or child. He'd lost his membership in the diplomatic community and was not going to risk the chance and travel. When Prince was old enough he started visiting his dad in the former Soviet Union. Soon he developed a relationship with his cousins who were members of the Mafia and became their main man on the island. Going back to the beginning of business, their barter trade kept both pockets eating like a fat woman at an all you can eat restaurant.

More seriously though, with the help of the Russian Mafia, we would be able to size up our Italian friends. Price took care of the necessary arrangements and we paid for the mercenaries who were now on their way to the USA awaiting our return. All we had to do was stack guns and ammo like the Matrix, find an out of town spot and finally put an end to a war that we now had a chance of winning. We all wanted to pay Prince for all that he'd done for us. If it had not been for him and Buju, we would have followed our ego and maybe lost our lives.

All he wanted was for us to make a promise that we would one-day return and invest in the island. At the airport, he gave Blade an envelope and asked him not to open until mid-air. We said our farewell and were off. The envelope Blade was holding had an old picture of a pregnant woman holding a bunch of banana. Possibilities are it was a picture of his mother.

# Chapter Eleven

We entered the USA via Miami, switched flights to Philly and hit route 130 in a two-hour traffic drive back to NY. We later rented a mansion in Montclair Newark and set up base. Mr. Eastwood had already taken care of that. He had good credit. In America you have to have good credit. Our Russians had already blended with society as cab drivers and slaughtered a few Gambinos. I'll tell you again, any identity needed Kevin could make it. We were transported by them and only. You can never be at war and be high profile. Keep it on the down low, no more being in the spotlight.

First, we had to hit them where it hurts most. The ones they most cared for. No women and kids involved. Tavina was off da hook. No invention convention could host the unique bombs she invented. We intercepted their phone conversations and took advantage of opportunities. A Sprint dealership was to deliver a new flip phone for Tony Wongs head of security. Tavina waited outside their office for the delivery person and signed for the package. She then carefully planted the device in the phone and made the delivery. Less than an hour later, a bomb exploded killing not only him, but also five others that were in his office. Dialing the seventh digit had triggered the bomb. Who knows, a bomb could be in the Sprint phone you have. Your call. Beauty and brains is indeed a very dangerous combination, one that made me attracted to her.

Another informer sold us who and where to find Mr. Wongs main accountant and we set out to get him. He was an overweight bloated looking beast. He loved to eat pizza, Dominoes. Tavina broke into the biology lab in the college near our camp and created whatever it is that she did. We waited about five blocks from his house for two days. While Tavina and I were waiting for the delivery car to come by, we started a conversation. That's how I realized we had alot in common. Then I began to get personal. I asked her if she had a boy friend and she said yes. Then I told her that there is a big difference between having a man and a boy friend. I told her that a boyfriend means that she was still looking for a man. She smiled. The first smile I had seen since I met her. She said he bought her all she needed while she was in school while she saved the money her dad sent her. The bad thing was that he was a total failure in bed. To make up for his missing inches he ate her pussy. She said it was the only thing she had to look forward to. Soon he became bad at doing the only thing he seemed to be good at sexually, so she dumped him. I asked her what does she do to keep her hormones from driving her crazy and she replied masturbate. Then she told me how she used to get so wet she had to wear panty liners to stop the overflow of her natural juices. She said her pussy stayed wet.

"Can I see and feel how wet it is"?

She thought I was joking. Then I took her hands and let her hold my pipe. I was hard as a rock. She was wearing a short Baby Phat skirt with a blouse that showed her nipples. She saw me looking at them and told me not to be afraid to touch. That is where she went wrong. Then she turned to me and opened her legs. She was not wearing any panties. She said they made her feel uncomfortable, especially when around some one as fine as me. She had a fatty. I started rubbing her legs and worked my way up to her thighs, then I slid my finger into her, and she felt so warm. She started groaning. While one hand was busy inside her the other was taking the condom out my pocket. She had a body like J-Lo, only black. I did not bother to take off my pants, just in case she may want to change her mind. I was too horny to let that happen. Don't ask me how, but we ended up on the back seat, good thing my Durango has plenty of room.

I spread her legs and slowly, slowly entered her. I had to take my time, she was too tight and do I have a lot to put in. The last time a girl measured it I was almost twelve inches. Honestly. She felt so good it made me forget where we were, the mission we were on and most importantly, how dangerous she was. Position after position until we started sweating. Then I laid on my back and let her get on top. It was like fire works. She had all the right moves. I looked at her, but she had her eyes closed. Then she screamed again. Another organism. That was the fifth time and each time she dug her fingernails in my back, this time it was my chest. This time I put her on her knees and let her hug the seat. Doggy style. All up in her belly, I could feel my dick touching her walls, and then I felt the blood rushing through my vein. I grabbed her hair and wrapped it around my hands; her braids were beginning to fall out. I started to stroke her faster and faster, trying to get deeper and deeper, giving her all I got. Out of impulse I just punched her in the back of her head. Then she screamed.

Even after I exploded into her I was still stroking. If it had not been for that fucking police officer whom came by knocking on the window, I could have gotten another chance to fuck her before she died.

About noon we saw a car with the popular slogan. I stopped the car and let Tavina handle her business, paid the deliveryman then bounced. I really wanted to finish what we started but she said once is enough.

Their beloved accountant's wife found her husband in bed the next morning with his belly swollen. That's why I don't eat from people. When heads began to turn, we laid back for three weeks. Our Russians had also claimed a few heads. Influential Chinese Mafia and businessmen were disappearing. Our drivers used to kidnap them by simply knocking them out, stealing cars putting them in the trunk and leaving them in long-term parking lots in the airport. They had to stop using the parking lots when a lot attendant went to investigate the terrible smell from the trunk of 1996 Nissan Maxima. Investigators found more than 10 cars. Some trucks having double occupancy. Instead of using the airport parking lots, they began buying old cars and dumping them in junkyards out of state.

What goes around comes around. Bugs and Daffy was on a stake out at a club in Long Island. That's where Tony Wong and his gang hung out. They had been using the same red Honda civic and with all the disappearances, everyone who came in their vicinity became a suspect. One Saturday night after their target left the club with his clan, they followed them trying to find out where our beloved lived. A few blocks down their limo yield at a stoplight and so did our boys about five cars behind. Before the light turned green two motorcycles pulled alongside them and opened fire. They never stood a chance. Now we were down by two.

Mr. Eastwood was also taken. He didn't loose his life on the streets, but he was sent to prison. A regular customer found specimen of meats not poultry related. He was sentenced to five years in prison. At his hearing in court, a woman testified that on a Sunday when most people prepare their most healthy meal of the week, she bought some pork from the meat shop. She said she was in a hurry to prepare her meal, as she had to get to work later that evening. She went in details to tell the court that she had already cooked the rice and peas and was about to start frying her meat. She said the smell was just not the same and she knows that there is nothing wrong with her cooking. Upon investigation, she realized the upper half of a finger stuck in a piece of meat.

She said that she took it to Mr. Eastwood who did nothing but invited her inside the meat shop. She thought he was being smart so she called the cops. The only thing that saved him was his good reputation and the fact that he said it could have come from his distributor. He was charged for not inspecting the product before selling it. If they only knew, in fact, if she only knew what she missed by not going in the meat shop.

When word of his misfortune got out, it sent a wave of disbelief across his community, almost causing a riot. They refused to accept the allegations being brought against what was seen as a very kind family oriented family man and community activist. Despite the commotion, no one came forward to pay his twenty thousand dollars bail. By now the winter was in full effect. To make matters worst three of our contracted killers had lost their lives, their bodies and motive for their mysterious deaths are yet to be found.

Slime had a real problem keeping his dick in his pants. We left him and Tavina one afternoon. When we returned the next day, he had already raped her repeatedly. In fear of what his punishment would be for his unexpected betrayal he disappeared. To think I was entertaining thoughts of enjoying her again. Now she too probably has AIDS. I really do not want to confirm those thoughts. I guess once is enough. A few weeks later, we got a call from a bar in Trenton near Diamonds. He had been drinking at their annual

Christmas party and was in no condition to drive home. Miracles do happen in Christmas. Tavina made him a gift and we went to get him.

When we got there, he was wasted, drunk beyond state limitations. We took him to the Brooklyn Bridge with the gift she'd made. We didn't even bother to do any bodily harm to him. Tavina put the bomb in his pants and set the detonator for fifteen seconds. We backed off and told Rocky to push him, Slime grabbed on to Rocky belt and both of them exploded. Rocky was beginning to have doubts about what the outcome of this war would be anyway. If you're going to do anything and have doubts, then don't. You may end up like Rocky.

His family had already deserted him after they found out about his substance abuse, so no one made a big deal about it. Slimes family was unknown, so that was no problem.

The game plan was to shake up the Chinese camp and force them to back off so we could allow Blade to settle his score with Roberto Tusscanni.

We were invited to Cari-Fest in Brooklyn hosted by Legendary Records. The biggest one day show in north America. I thought that had the right to earn event of the year. The line up included Capleton, Elephant Man, George Nooks, Richie Stephens, Wayne Wonder, Mary J. Blidge, Eve, Hawkeye and Ghost. We pulled up in all white. Keep in mind that it had just finished raining lightly and the glow from the lights of the glowing extra stretched Lex limo made us look like money with life.

So fresh and so clean. When we pulled up it was all eyes on us. You may not believe this, but by the end of the night, I had Mary's phone number. Honestly I do to this very day.

We had the felt hats with the feathers, tailor made suits and Tims. That's right Timberland boots. Our carriage female drivers and escorts brought us the crock and socks at the entrance so we could make an entrance. There was a small crowd outside, not a long line. Patrons were not paying to get in, most of them complained that the asking price of thirty dollars for admission was too much. Not everyone is in the street pharmacy game. Nine-five people have a budget and want to have fun. We sent a message via our accountant to open the gates and free up the bar. None of us could walk into a store and get candy on credit, but in the streets we had A1 credit. The show delivered as promised and expected.

During the last of the Scare Dem crew's performance, the communities wanna be don saw Rice and D messing with his cousins and decided to become a cock blocker.

He walked over and grabbed, I think her name was Shaday, by her hands and told her to leave. Rice offered him $500 just to leave her alone. He took it personal. He told Rice if he had the guts to meet him out side the venue. The performances was now over and the sound systems, Stone Love, Hell Razor, Tony Matteron, and Q-45. Kept the crowd around to listen to their thirty-minute segments. Rice gave a woman two hundred to get his license plate number. By the second segment, there was an announcement that a BMW plate number AZ546P was blocking some ones car and the person wants to_leave. Ready to brag that he was the owner of the car in question, he left to release the driver. He went outside and that was the last time they saw him. Where is Mr. Eastwood when you need a meat shop?

While on our way to our very own after hour spot, one of our pay roll precinct members told us that they had just arrested Tony Wong for drunk driving and that he had just called his lawyer. That meant the he would be out soon.

At the exact time we got there he was just leaving. We waited until he and his lawyer pulled off. We followed them to her office. They got to the location and had been sitting outside about twenty minutes before she came out. I could swear she was giving him a blowjob. We waited until she went inside and then approached him. Blade went over to his car, pulled the door and pulled him out. In the blink of an eye, he must have kicked Blade like fifty times.

"Is what the fuck this? Bombo-clat Jet Li?"

Then the fight started. No one interrupted. Rice wanted to join in, but David told him to make it a fair fight. Blade never stood a chance in hell. He did give him a few punches, but none of them seemed to be of much significance. After taking maybe ten minutes of beating, he came to the car to get his baseball bat. Then it became a fair fight. At first he made a few wild swings, but Wong was too swift, so he timed his movement. The first hit he got was in his neck. That sent him to the ground. Then he started working on his knees. When he thought he had made him weak enough, he started fighting with his hands. One lesson I learnt was that you couldn't fight a black belt or a boxer with your hands. You have to use a weapon to make it a fair fight.

We slit his tongue and tied his hands behind him to his feet. He was bleeding too much so we covered his mouth with duct tape. D took the sword he bought as a part of his ninja collection and pushed a quarter of the blade into his spinal cord. They found him in the back seat of a Grey hound bus on its way to Washington. When they relived him, he was seemingly beginning to be killed, just to ease the pain. He was already crippled for life.

By the second day of his death, six Italians and four Chinese had lost their lives all in a crossfire dispute over who was responsible for Wrong's death. The plan was to turn them against each other and it seemed to be working. Now all we had to do is take them out big to small. If you cut of a chicken head, the body just runs around with no direction and soon dies. Laws of Nature.

It was time to bring the heat. Time to test the hands of faith and let destiny reveal itself. Thug style Mortal Combat, kill or be killed. I called my wife and told her that I may not be around much longer. She may not have shown that she loved me, but I still loved her. I made sure that all I had would be divided equally among my kids. I would hate for any of them to feel I loved one more than the other. My only request was that when they last see my face, they should not cry. Lavita and Roberto were having their son christened at a cathedral on Market St. in Philadelphia. They wanted to be cautious, but we had already gotten the down low on the days event. We decided to strike all out. We went in two separate cars. The first had our three Russians, Kevin and Tavina. The second had Blade, David and me. As soon as we crossed the Ben Franklin Bridge, one of my tires blew out. Luckily we weren't in heavy traffic and I was able to regain control.

Thank God I have triple A. Blade told Tavina to go ahead and we would be there as soon as we changed tires.

When we got to Market St. there was a huge crowd surrounding the yellow tape boundary and almost every law enforcement personnel in the city was securing the vicinity. I asked the owner of a nearby store what had happened, he said a group opened fire on a car with four men and a lady. When we went to see the car. It had more holes than a pair of fish net stockings. The entire thing was a plot to kill us. If they knew we were coming, they also knew our location. If our tire hadn't blown out we would have been on our way to hell.

If the investigators put all the information together, all fingers would be pointed towards us. The death of a FBI agent, a prominent Italian businessman and three illegal aliens, unsolved murders, the slaying of the most feared voodoo priest and his family, and not to mention the bodies of what seemed to be law abiding Chinese professionals.

We had no choice but going on the run. We left the mansion in Montclair and rented a rundown project building in Orange, NJ.

We occupied the 3rd and 4th floors, recruited eight street thugs and regrouped. One night Diamond kept paging Blade 911 constantly. We only communicated by pagers, using numbers as words. We decided to pay her a visit and prepared for the worst. When we got there Diamond was sitting in her car covered with blood, she was perfectly fine, but there were six dead bodies in her house. All the whores on day shift were slaughtered each body with more than five shots. There was a note written in blood.

"Just as I killed your FBI bitch and the others, your turn next."

Blade left immediately and didn't return until sunrise the next day. The New York post headline read…

"Daughter of deceased drug lord slain."

Her skull and every possible bone cracked, murder weapon said to be a hammer. A note was also found. What goes around comes around. Investigators said they had already begun looking into her mysterious death and had opened a further investigation onto the death of Don Deangelo. Word on the streets was that they offered a protection program to her newly wed husband and child.

Roberto had killed possibly the only woman he would ever love, so he just did the same, simple and plain. What goes around comes around. Diamond called the cops and told them that someone had broken into her house and killed her sisters' kids who were visiting her from Daytona Beach. After giving all the information she thought was necessary to book the case as a homicide. She went into a zone. She stop speaking and started acting crazy. The investigators bought it and put her in a mental institution. She was tired and could use the rest and pampering anyway. They say you have to have a college degree to be smart. Diamond never been finished high school, but outsmarted the top investigators assigned to the NYPD. New York's finest. You go girl. Just stay away from those pills.

The letter that the Don gave to Blade shortly before he died contained a phone number and the name of the only person in Howard Beach that Blade could trust. Vito Gurino II. He was the son of the legendary hitman Vito "Socko" Gurino. At 300 pounds, his dad had a neck the size of a watermelon. For Target practice, he used to shoot the heads of chickens running around his backyard.

His father had double-crossed the Colombo crime family and as a result they killed him, his mother, his two sisters and brother. Although he was only nine years old when he witnessed his family being slaughtered, he was smart enough to lie in the pool of blood from his sisters' body as if he too had been shot. At that time Don Deangelo was only a captain, so his duty was to dispose of the bodies. Halfway across town, he heard a knocking in the trunk of his van. He pulled over to investigate, the kid was still alive Don Deangelo had a big heart, he took the kid as his own. At age 19, he took on the responsibility of raising a child that he should have killed if found alive, not only that, but he also put himself and his family in danger of also being killed.

Only the two knew the truth and kept it as such. Now known as Louis, he established himself as a personal cook. His authentic Italian dishes were favored by many. He visited the local market on Mondays so he could get all the fresh produces from the previous weekend. We awaited his arrival and took him to the back of the market. Blade quickly outlined what was going on, gave him the Dons ring and the letter. He assured Blade that Roberto would pay for what he had done.

On February 18, 2002, Roberto had an all star party to celebrate his thirty fifth birthday. Members of the Gambino and Colombo crime families, along with specially invited dons from across the country were present to share in the festivities. Louis was assigned a few apprentices and ordered to prepare a meal fit for kingpins. Due to his tremendous skills, the apprentices kept their eyes peeled and watched his every move. This allowed him to only poison the food at random plates. Unfortunately, Tusscanni survived. The poison was rare and could only be triggered by drinking water, after which the victim had six days to live. By the end of the month eight members of the respective crime families had lost their lives. Autopsy showed the remainder of a virus that was still eating the intestine.

When they finally figured out what was going on. Louis was already fastening his seatbelt and heading to the home of the real Mafioso. The old country. Midway across the Mediterranean Sea, there was Blade by his side. The phone number was actually the code to a vault where the Don kept the few things he'd kept a record of. Besides his documents, there was a tape that would destroy anyone who crossed him and his seal. All these were to be taken to the real head of the crime family in Palermo, Sicily.

Blade had left unexpectedly. For weeks no one knew where he was and no communication. On July 28, I got the news that my wife was dead. I knew who killed her. Sameta. I was talking to her for about a year. She was a bank teller. So as not to become too suspicious of depositing large sums of money I did frequently, I would just take the money to her and she did the rest. She was an educated woman living in the ghetto. That song that Jay-Z did, girls, girls. Sameta was the project chick that played her part. I met her at a party one night. She grew to love me beyond love. She would do anything for me, wherever we went she would carry my gun. Always keeping it gansta. My birthday is August first. A year ago she told me she would marry me three days after my birthday. One night I was at her house watching Comic View and she asked me why don't I love her as much as she does me? I did not answer. I guess she realized that only one woman had the keys to my heart, my wife, so she did what she thought would be in her best interest.

I went to make a deposit and they told me she was on vacation. A week later she returned. Just two days before my birthday, on my birthday I went to her house for dinner. During the meal, she handed me a box and I opened it. My heart began to cry. It was my wife wedding ring. I looked at her and she signaled me to put it on her finger. She said that is how much she loved me. Her lips were moving but my ears were listing to the words of my heart as it cried. I had a 9mm in my waist with a silencer on it. From where she was sitting, her back was to the wooden wall padded with cushion. Then she stopped talking; looked at me with tears in her eyes, whispered she loved me, then slowly put her head on the table. I had given her all six shots. It was bad enough I was cheating on her, now I was the cause of her death. Honey if you hear me from heaven, I am really sorry and I will mourn you until we meet in the life after death, if there is one. While Blade had mysteriously disappeared, Rice had captivated the minds of our new soldiers and started his own monarchy. They went on some senseless robbing sprees, started fights in clubs just for fun, all the things that brought unwanted attention to our name.

D and I had no choice but to roll with the pack, not because we wanted or had to, but to keep a close finger on some trigger-happy cold blooded idiots. Rice called an emergency meeting. He and his bunch of animated thugs showed up high and drunk smelling like cheap cigar. After reminding us of where we were coming from, he gave us his vision of the future. Death, we all would be. Unless we killed Blade. He outlined that if we killed Blade then we could all get out and start over with our own individual lives, especially since he had already deserted us.

David was the fist to respond.

"Kill Blade? Nigga you fucking crazy? How the fuck you want to kill the only person you had to turn to when yu people dem kick yu out a dem place? Since you can kill a dead man, you have enough help, so you don't need me go ahead, I won't have anything to do with your plans. In fact, if I didn't know you for so long, I would shoot you right here and now. Who the fuck was there for you when your family turned their back on you? What about all the shit him and me had to save you from. If I was in his position, you would want to do the same to me."

D started walking towards Rice slowly. Then when he was close enough he punched him in his face. One of his boys pulled out his gun and I shot him. All the others didn't bother to move. I made it clear. If both of them have a problem, let them fight it out one will win, let them do it among themselves. I know that David was happy he finally had a good reason to fuck him up. I stood there and watched them fight until, they were both tired and bloody. I wouldn't say that one or the other won the fight. They were both men enough to give some good punches and kicks. David left, but before he did, he told Rice that he would remember him in his prayers and all those who would choose to confront Blade. His last words were seven times rise and seven times fall. He looked Rice dead in his eyes and told him he won't be the last man standing. I stayed. If anyone had a chance to determine the out come of all this, it would be me. As for the kid that got shot, he left and told me we would one day meet again I am yet to see him, but I am somewhat prepared for the unexpected.

From that point on, I told them I would keep all guns and ammo. Since things were going through a period of uncertainty, I wanted to be extra careful. You can never be prepared for what people will do to you. Especially those you cant trust in the dark. Keeping the guns was just taking extra precautions. You know, just in case.

Rice and his boys kept running in and out of jail. Starting uncalled for bar fights, grabbing on peoples women, ordering moet and cris for him and his goons and not paying. He was just totally out of control; I should have killed him myself. Blade returned a few weeks later. He never told us where he was or what he was up to; he just called a meeting. One I was almost sure was going to be our final one. He told Rice to meet him at his house. In fact, we all were to meet him there. Rice didn't bother to mention what had happened between him and David. I was at my house when Rice and his crew came to deliver the message. I was cooking some shrimp and steamed vegetables and they all sat down to enjoy the Last Supper.

Before we left I asked Rice exactly what was he up to. He said he was just basically tired of being treated like he is lesser than any of us. Blade would sometimes talk to him in a disrespectful manner, but that was just being himself. Whenever Rice is in the streets, people talked to him in a polite manner and treated him with respect. Around us he seemed to be the latter of the pack. Go to the liquor store, park the car, cook this, and bag that, the orders he got were endless, so he wanted to put an end to them. He wanted freedom and respect; tonight he had the nerves to ask for it. When we got to Blades house everyone took a gun for himself. I kept them at my house and had put them in the trunk of my car. Due to frequent police harassment, none of them carried guns. I had my glock and an extra clip; all the other guns had blank shots. I had to have the extra edge; maybe tonight my opportunity would knock. While Blade was waiting for us inside, we were outside his plotting to kill him. The only thing I asked was that no one shoot him in his head.

There was a jeep parked a block down with an unidentified person, so we had to make sure we didn't make too much noise or look too suspicious. We went in and Blade seemed comfortable lying in his coffin, what a place to be and what a time to be there. He asked me for David and I told him he must have been out of town on some personal interest. He didn't seem to buy that story, but he said nothing more on the topic. Then he realized how Rice was pacing the floor. If you knew him, then you would know something was bothering him.

He didn't even bother to ask who the strangers were. As soon as the last person entered the room and closed the door, a candle blew out. Blade looked at it and smiled, then he stepped out his coffin and asked me to turn over the basins of blood he had in the corners. He then had a drink of Jamaican rum and went back to lay back in his coffin.

Rice was still pacing the floor so he called him to find out what was on his mind. He pulled out his glock and pointed it a Blade, who then smiled at him.

"So, you finally have the balls to step up to the plate? How much longer were you planning to be a pussy? You always wanted to be like me. You walk like me, talk like me and even try to dress like me. Do you know why you can't be like me? Some of us are made to rule; rejects like you were designed to follow. The fact is I will forever be Nino and you will remain G. Money. You can never be a boss, your nothing but a fucking punk, bitch."

Without responding, Rice stepped to him and smacked him with his gun. You could see the blood leaking from the side of his mouth. He tried to hide the pain but it showed. By now, Blade was slowly sitting up.

1 "O lord my God, in thee do I put my trust: save me from all them that prosecute me and deliver me: 2 lest he tear my soul like a lion, rending it in pieces, where there is none to deliver."
Every one looked at each other and then at him.
"What the fuck is he doing?"
He was repeating Psalms 7.
Verse 6 "Arise, O Lord in thine anger, lift up thyself because of the rage of mine enemies: and awake for me to the judgement that thou...."
Suddenly like magic, Blade took a sword from the side of his coffin and with one swing; Rice head was on the floor and his body grasping for life. His gang opened fire, hitting Blade in his chest more than... I don't know how many times, he just fell back and the lid on the coffin closed.

Without thinking, I opened fire on them unexpectedly. By the time any of them realized that the guns were loaded with blanks, they were all dead men. They always underestimated me, most people do, but trust me, I will do things to you that will make heaven cry and mourn.

Everyone thought I was of a less violent nature, now I can hear their spirits in hell saying if they only knew then, they would be alive now. I always do my dark deeds by myself, that way I don't have to worry about some coward telling who, when, where or why I killed. With very little time to get out of town, I took him out the coffin, put his body in my Durango and set the house on fire. I had to go back to my house so I could get a change of clothes; blood was all over me. I came back to the truck and Blades body was gone. I didn't know what to do. I know he got shot, but I needed the body to make sure he was dead. What if he was not dead and managed to get out? Where would he go? Shit!

A few minutes later the police were all over the place. They brought me downtown for questioning. They had been watching us for a long time, a very long time. Now they wanted answers for unanswered questions. I told them that I was just a cook at the restaurant and everyone was dead. Blade, David, Rice, Industry, they were all dead. Then they asked me if I knew anything about a body found in an empty apartment in Staten Island. They said the body belonged to a college student that had been reported missing. I started thinking by myself; if the body they found really belonged to a missing college student, then what happened to Industry? I just played the fool so I could catch the wise. I told them that all I know is that there was a big shoot out and no one came out alive. They had bodies in Blades burnt out house, so they had no choice but to believe me and close the case. As far as the charges against us, I told them that the people responsible were also killed in the fire.

They kept me detained for a few more hours then let me go with a warning. A few days before the funeral an unidentified person bailed Mr. Eastwood. Diamond miraculously regained her sense when she got word that Blade was killed. After convincing the doctors she was well enough to be released, she came and joined the many that were mourning the death of a Don.

They all wanted to see his body but I told them that would not be a good idea as he was burnt very badly. I had no choice but to tell them that his body was burnt in the fire, what else could I have said or done? On September twentieth we gathered to pay our last respects and say our final good-bye. Mr. Brown and his wife paid a very surprising visit, even the Feds showed up to make sure that a suspect they were unable to touch for more than 7 years was gone once and for all. While at the funeral, there was an unidentified person standing maybe 80ft away in a black trench coat and hat, they never came close. Diamond and Mr. Eastwood bid their final good-byes.

"He that overcommeth shall inherit all things, and I will be his God and he shall be my son. Ashes to ashes and dust to dust."

Those were the final words before gunshots broke the bitter silence as we said good-bye to a real Jamaican don.

After the funeral I got news that 4 Italians came for Roberto and took him back to the old country for trail. If convicted he'd face death by way of a firing squad; the other godfathers of the mob were to be jury. David moved to Canada, he said he wanted to be away from it all. He was the only person that missed the funeral. He escaped to be where he could stay cold and be isolated. Without Blade he was lost, so he moved to a new territory to start a new life. Even though I'd done what I could to stop them, someone may have had a live round in his gun. I made sure to change the clips and replace them with blanks. Where and what had happened to his body? I have no idea. I got a visa for my kids and moved to California. Where the sticky green would keep my mind off things.

D and I kept in touch at least once or twice per month. The last time I spoke to him he had a 2-year-old son and another on the way. Canada was good for him. He liked to be cold. He was going back to school so he could extend his mental capacity. Him having a wife and child changed him. He sounded more calm and relaxed. Most of our conversations were short. We both avoided talking about what happened. I think that he was avoiding the reality of all the events that made him mature so quickly and that ended so mysteriously. Now that I have done what I came to do, I can get on with my life. What am I talking about? It was me. I did it. I was the one that shot Blade. I was the only one with a live round. Why did I do it? Remember Ras Silk? He was my brother. Not by blood, but by being best friend. Let me explain. When they sent Armani to kill him, I was the one who saved his life and killed Armani. I used to work in Burger King. He came in and robbed the place one day and took my white gold chain. I had saved for too long to make him just take it. I waited until he exited and busted his windows as he left. Two days later we ran into each other at the liquor store. Some how we became friends. My job was not enough to support my family; he introduced and educated me to the drug game. Slowly we became the ghetto stars. I had ideas with unlimited income possibilities and he had the way to fund them. He sold the drugs and I used the income to make profitable business investments. We saved until we bought a restaurant and rented a club. Soon we had our own franchise. When Armani shot the driver and his friend, the Ras was not the one that killed him, the Ras never carried a gun, and he hated guns. I was a few cars behind when he tried to start his daylight-killing spree. Remember the Beemer that came to a halt? That was I. We were on our way to Atlantic City and I was just a few cars behind. Before he had a chance to kill my life long and only friend, he was killed. I told the Ras that we needed to get out of town, but he was never the one to run from a fight. I knew something was going to go down. They hanged him by his locks from the bridge so Philly could see him. We made a promise to look out for each other and now that he is dead I had to honor him. When I met Blade, all I wanted to do was kill him, but I had to wait for the perfect time. I became like an undercover police in too deep. Far too deep. In order for me to get revenge I had to become like them. Eat, drink, sleep, talk, walk and even kill for them. Whatever it took to get the job done. At one point I was almost beginning to loose sight of what my purpose of being with them was. It was like becoming a new me, a me I now hate. Not for what I did, but for what I put myself through to get it done. Now he is dead and I still cant go on with my life. I hated the devil and now I have become him. A few months ago I started to make a diary of my life. Maybe one day the world will be able to share my pain. Spelling has always been my weak point so please forgive me, I have more important things to worry about. Two days ago I almost shot my own kid for trying to surprise me. What have I become? Most of the fish scale they thought Industry stole, I did it. He stole a small amount, but that was the amount I set up for him to steel. Why do you think I kicked him down the steps so quickly? I was selling to small time drug dealers in up state Albany. All my money was sent to Jamaica. I renovated and rented houses on the island, bought a club, named it Club Pleasure and opened a shoe store. I made sure all my kids could attend school and not worry about ever paying school fees. This life is not a promise to any of us, so the time I have on this earth I made sure they would be able to enjoy the things I wish I were able to. They never ever expected it, but how could they? I didn't kill him much earlier because if I made the move at the wrong time, they would have gotten drunk, get high, and then beat me to death.

The story of how I got to NY was just that, a story. Many of the things they told me were lies also. This is only 1/3 of my diary. The remainder of my story is fully explained. I have already made arrangements for it to be delivered in the event that they find me before I am able to finish them. My only regret is that David got away. Some how I feel this story is far from over. I hope not. I began my own rule of terror, In my mind it had all ended, in reality it was still here.

I started my own company. I promised my mother that I would become a lawyer, but now I have found a passion for the entertainment business. New Image Entertainment. It was only two years old and growing with a few talented artists. I got married to our accountant who gave birth to our son on Boxing Day of last year. Now my life was seemingly getting back to being a normal one. For the first time I was beginning to know what it feels like to be happy, I even gained a few pounds from the delicious home cooked meals I enjoyed. I was on my way home from a nerve-racking day at the office. Our system was down for two hours or more and my office manger quit.

After a day of total disappointment, all I wanted to do was go home. Then my cell phone rang I was not in the mood to talk to anyone so I let the answer machine pick up. No message. The same thing happened again and again, still the caller left no message. Due to the problem of over crowding, traffic on the turnpike was no joke. My office was only fifty minutes away and it took more than an hour to get there in the mornings. Going home took nearly twice that time. I was definitely not in the mood for someone playing mystery caller.

The phone rang again. This time I picked up.

"What the eyes see and what the ears hear, the mind believes. Always remember, the greatest trick the devil ever pulled was convincing the world he did not exist."

I was confused for a minute.

"Who the fuck is this?"

The caller started laughing. I hung up. I really did not let it bother me; besides, the number came up as unlisted, so I could not redial. About five minutes later the phone rang again. This time it was David. He said that he was in Philly.

"What the hell you doing in Philly?"

He said that he received a package a week ago with a map of Philly and an X marked spot. He said that he also got a call, but until he was sure, he could not tell me who it was. I told him that I was on my way home and would meet him in Philly in two days. What the fuck is happening. Well, I guess the opportunity to kill him was here.

I called my crib and told my wife to take the kids and spend the night at the hotel. She was very worried, but she also knew that at any given moment anything could and can happen. That was what made me like her so much. She had the ability to understand the man she has and has unlimited faith in me. I got to Philly a day later than expected. I all most walked past David. The last time I saw him, he was no more than 6ft 2in weighing about 165lbs. Now I was looking at a 210-pound muscle man.

"You sure you're not coming from prison?"

I was thinking of stabbing him to death. I don't think that will work now. He smiled and gave me a pound and handed me the package.

"Are you sure there is no Anthrax on it?"

A few years ago anthrax had killed a few people, so I had to make sure. The spot on the map was an abandoned Catholic Church in German Town. D had no idea of who or where the packages came from, but who ever sent it knew where and how to locate him. Then my phone rang again. This time it was an automated message telling me to enter the holy temple at the rear. I told them what the message said.

After a short debate of the main possibilities of what could happen, we went to the back of the church. The back door was already opened. We went in and I put my gloves on. Ready to strike at first chance. The place was darker than night. Then a sign said turn left. The left turn led to the basement and there were basins of blood every where.

"What the fuck is this? I don't know about you, but I am going home. If you want, you can wait for who ever sent you the treasure map".

David said he was also leaving. He got to the steps, looked up and passed out. I went to see what or whom he saw and I could not believe my eyes...

To be continued...

Coming Soon

THE RISE AND FALL OF A JAMAICAN DON
- THE RETURN

**Also coming soon from Andre Porter**

TEARS FROM MY PEN

A COLLECTION OF POETRY AND SHORT STORIES
ALSO FEATURING NEW AUTHORS
(Big up Kirlew....The Ghetto Shakespare from
Bronx NY)

Twenty-five to life
A detailed interview of women married to drug-lords and
the love of pain they suffer.

The diary of a Jamaican; love, pain and survival.
I ALSO HAVE TWO KIDS BOOK ALREADY
COMPLETED
"WHEN IS DADDY COMING HOME?"
&
"DO YOU LOVE MOMMY?"

# About The Author

Heights by great men reached and kept were not attained by sudden flight, but I while my companions slept, kept toiling onwards through the night .My name is Andre Porter, I was born on January 18, 1977 in Kingston Jamaica to two young adults to whom I am grateful. They matured and raised me to be the determined and confident person I am. After living most of my life in Kingston, I moved to Westmoreland. At age ten, I was awarded a government scholarship to the number one school on the island, Jamaica College. After moving to Western Jamaica, I got a transfer to Cornwall College where I started my journey to become a lawyer. I graduated among the ten students voted most likely to be successful. Instead of trying to avoid the obstacles my parents made sure I got the education to, I faced them head on. I had a natural charm that still never fails to melt any woman's heart or give me the extra edge when I needed it. I was not accepted into Rugters University Law School here in Camden New Jersey and with a few months left to be a father once more, I choose to work to support the family. I had began to create. After experiencing my first emotional struggle, I decided to use the pain to fuel my dreams. *THE RISE AND FALL OF A JAMAICAN DON* is just one of the many stories that I have fabricated in order to introduce you and the world to me. I have a deep passion for cooking, poetry, and music of all forms and most importantly dancing. As apart of my contribution towards community development, I have built the ANDRE PORTER FOUNDATION for kids. Its main aim is to help those students whose parents are not able to afford the cost of allowing them to attend school on a regular basis. I am the oldest of four sisters and two brothers, and also a very proud father to the kids that heaven knows I dreamed of. Like John Q, I will do what it takes to make them eat. This is my first published work and I hope you will find it to be as entertaining as I intended it to be. Enjoy.